Lucie F. Stafford
Christmas 1923

Stories and Poems
FROM
The Old North State

Edited by

MRS. STURGIS ELLENO LEAVITT

Chairman of Literature (1921-1923)
North Carolina Federation of Women's Clubs

ILLUSTRATIONS BY HARRIET WILMOT CALDWELL

PRINTED BY
THE SEEMAN PRINTERY INCORPORATED
DURHAM, N. C.

TO

MARY LOUISA COOPER

CONTENTS

---

* Changed residence.

CONTENTS

INTRODUCTION

The material for this volume was collected in order to preserve the literary efforts of the women of the North Carolina Federation, and has been published with the hope of stimulating greater interest in creative writing in the state. Sympathy and understanding, not material rewards, are needed to encourage our writers to continue their work and if a measure of recognition is accorded them now we may some day be proud of a strong group of women writers representing North Carolina. The following selections should therefore be judged not as attempts to compete with the productions of authors whose reputation has already been established, but as the first strivings toward self expression of a group of women who desire to have their share in the intellectual life of the state.

The literary department to which these stories and poems were submitted came into being at the fifth convention held in Wilmington in 1907, at which Mrs. Eugene Reilley of Charlotte presided, the president, Mrs. J. T. Alderman, being seriously ill. At Mrs. Reilley's suggestion a literary department was formed and Miss Adelaide Fries of Winston-Salem elected chairman. Under her management the department weathered the difficulties of the first years and amply justified its creation.

During the year 1909-1910 Mrs. Reilley, then president of the federation, added new life to the literary department when, at her suggestion, the chairman of literature, Miss Fries, sent out a circular asking each club to submit articles for a "Paper Contest." In response to this call thirteen papers were presented which were divided into two groups, literary and historical, and placed in the hands of the judges, who selected one of each to be read at the annual convention on "Fine Arts Evening." The papers chosen were *The Viking Age,* by Mrs. W. L. Nicholson of Charlotte, and *The Development of the Drama,* by Mrs. W. C. A. Hammel of the Friday Afternoon Club of Greensboro. The success of this occasion was such that the federation voted to make Fine Arts Evening a permanent feature of its annual meetings.

The following year fourteen papers, representing ten clubs, were submitted, eight dealing with county history and six with the subject, "What study clubs are worth to North Carolina." The final selections were *Mecklenburg,* by Mrs. Paul Lucas of the Woman's Club of Charlotte, and a paper on study clubs by Mrs. Frank Martin of the Winston-Salem Sorosis Club.

For the club year 1911-1912 the papers in the historical group were restricted to the subject "Virginia Dare" and a call for poems was sent out. In response ten historical papers and twenty-five poems were received. The paper selected was written by Miss Helen Montague of the Woman's Reading Club of Winston-Salem and this was read at the convention together with three poems, *The Phantom Gold* (best short poem), by Mrs. Groom McNinch of the Woman's Club of Charlotte, *The Mother* (best long poem), by Mrs. Eugene Glenn of the Woman's Club of Asheville, and *Mammy,* by Miss S. O'H. Dickson.

Encouraged by this response the chairman, Mrs. Frank Martin of Winston-Salem, continuing in office for a second year, asked the clubs to submit not only essays and poems but stories of two sorts, one the scene of which was to be laid in North Carolina and the other without restrictions. The following year fifteen clubs took part in the literary contest, *Limitations* and *Echoes,* by Mrs. Charles Ives of New Bern, being the winning poems, with one short story selected, *Across the Sauratown,* by Mrs. Gordon Finger of Charlotte. At this convention the retiring chairman of literature suggested that the best research work done by any club woman during the year be announced on Fine Arts Evening and that some tangible award, such as a loving cup, be given the winner in the literary contests. This suggestion seems to have fallen on barren soil for there is no record of any contests the following year. So many inquiries came in, however, that it was recommended that they be "reopened" for another year.

Ample evidence of the advisability of this step was shown by the number of entries for 1915, twenty-two in poetry, nine in the short story, and four in research. The winner of the poetry contest was Mrs. Charles Ives of New Bern, and Mrs. Zoe Kincaid Brockman of Gastonia was the successful entrant in the short story contest.

INTRODUCTION

From 1915 on, the contests have steadily increased in interest and since 1917 have been restricted to short stories and poems. The last to receive mention in the research field was Mrs. J. Oliver May, whose paper *The Evolution of Nash County* was read by her at the convention in 1917 and published later in the *Rocky Mount Telegram*. In 1917-1918 "because of the day's many demands upon the time and energy of the club women" it was decided to limit the contests to a prescribed patriotic theme. The entries for that year were few either due to the stir of many war activities or to the fact that the writers felt hampered by the limitation of subject. Of late the contests have had incentives of a very real sort. In 1919 a loving cup known as the Separk Poetry Cup was donated by Mr. J. H. Separk of Gastonia, who very generously stated that if the cup were won twice by the same person she should become the permanent owner and a new cup would be supplied. The first to be successful in this contest was Mrs. Zoe Kincaid Brockman of Gastonia who also received the award the following year, thus losing no time in becoming its possessor. In 1920 Mrs. Gordon Finger of Charlotte, presented to the federation in memory of the well-known editor, "Joe" Caldwell, the Joseph Pearson Caldwell Cup, to be awarded for the best short story. The first winner of the contest was Miss Susie Whitehead of Salisbury, with the story *The Soul of a Pilgrim*.

A third cup came to the federation in rather an unusual way. At the convention held in Greensboro in 1922 the chairman of literature, in reviewing the honors to be bestowed upon the successful entrants, inadvertently stated that there were *three* cups. At this the Honorary President, always mindful of her blundering flock, promptly rectified in a stage whisper —"Two." Recovering her composure the chairman remarked that though the federation had the Separk Cup and the Joseph Pearson Caldwell Cup it did not have the O. Henry Cup—yet! The spontaneous applause and general good feeling which followed was a clear indication that the third cup was not far away. The following morning the O. Henry Cup was promised. Greensboro, represented by the Kiwanis Club, had lived up to her reputation.

With the added incentive of the O. Henry Cup the number of entries in the contests reached one hundred and fifty-three in 1923. Not only this but the stories and poems were of sufficient excellence to warrant the inclusion in this volume of those that received favorable mention from the judges. Some from the 1922 contests were also deemed worthy of being included. It is unfortunate that three selections receiving first honor before 1915 could not be obtained. Except for this the list is complete. In this connection the editor wishes to gratefully acknowledge the splendid work done by Miss Martha Daughton, Chairman of Contests, 1921-23, who assisted in the collection of this material. Thanks are due to Mr. Raymond W. Adams of the English Department of the University of North Carolina, who rendered valuable aid on many occasions,

INTRODUCTION

and to the men of the English departments of Wake Forest, Trinity, North Carolina College for Women, and the University of North Carolina who judged the contests of 1922 and 1923 and whose interest in this volume has been an inspiration.

That our readers may peruse these selections with sympathy and understanding it may be well to mention the conditions under which some of our authors worked. One, most prolific and successful, penned her heart throbs in poetic form while sitting in her sun parlor bravely fighting the Great White Plague. One, a busy newspaper woman; another, an ambitious public school teacher; and another, a slip of a girl with two tiny children and an admiring husband, extend the list. Still another relates trying experiences in a rambling, old, "haunted" house, feeding six wood stoves, prodding a shiftless servant, and nursing a group of little children who had a faculty for collecting all the epidemics in town; from this muddle of unreliable servants, wood stoves and punctured ears there evolved a powerful sermon which led the judges of the contest to believe that she had been "tried by fire and found pure gold."

Free from commercialism and professionalism these writers have followed their impulse for self expression and if the compilation of their efforts inspires other club women to imitate their example this little volume will have fulfilled its mission.

ALGA E. LEAVITT.

FOREWORD

Literature is the visible blossom of an impulse to write. Ability, effort, and perseverance are all essential to the development of that impulse, and encouragement and appreciation should be its award.

The power to create can be cultivated, the imagination can be stimulated into successful action; but genius is often shrinking, and talent is often timid. So to encourage each soul to express itself is always commendable.

Beautiful thoughts expressed in beautiful words are just as artistic as beautiful landscapes painted on canvas. Both keep the world, and both should be welcomed and enjoyed by all. Hence this volume, which we hope will be recognized as an effort to promote literary progress.

Progress, like humanity, needs a three-fold development, the material, the mental, and the spiritual. North Carolina is making wonderful material progress, but the future will be incomplete unless mental and spiritual progress keep step with it, as all three are essential to permanence.

The North Carolina Federation of Women's Clubs has made a beginning. Hope, persistence, and faith in their ideals, will keep them striving for the triple development necessary to make our state literature worthy and permanent.

SALLIE SOUTHALL COTTEN.

STORIES AND POEMS

FROM

THE OLD NORTH STATE

A SINGIN' LAD

BY

ZOE KINCAID BROCKMAN

——

Awarded Second Honor in 1915

A SINGIN' LAD

He was a lad from an Irish town,
A blue-eyed lad with a smilin' brow,
An', brushin' aside the mists o' woe
That cling to my past, I can see him now,

His sweepin' lashes an' gold-flecked hair,
An' lips that curved in a wistful way,
So that his smile wrapped round your heart
Like the misty shine o' an April day.

An' the voice o' him when he'd sing a song,
The lilt o' his voice and the swing o' the tune,
It would carry you up, an' on, an' on,
Till you kissed the fairies that light the moon.

An' then he would sit an' brood an' brood
With the whole o' dreamland in his eye,
As tho' he could hear in his heart the rime
O' the clingin' shadows driftin' by.

Ah, but he was the lad to love,
But he thought o' it light, an' he went his way;
And he left an echo to break my heart,
Adrift in the shades o' the twilight grey.

THE GREAT WHITE LAW

BY

ZOE KINCAID BROCKMAN

———

Awarded First Honor in 1916

THE GREAT WHITE LAW

THE CLANG of the heavy street doors of the bank at the customary closing hour brought a distinct sense of relief. I was very weary. A series of petty annoyances throughout the day had left me nerve-raw and fatigued. As I drew on my coat and passed out through a side entrance into the street I reflected that the position of cashier in a large and flourishing city bank is scarcely one to be envied.

Once outside I drew a long, luxuriant breath, the scent of freedom sweet in my nostrils. After all, it was long until another day. The crisp air enlivened and refreshed me, and beneath its crispness was a teasing hint of the coming spring. Violets were to be seen, lifting purple, prophetic faces above the freshened grass in many park spaces.

Boarding a car at Second Avenue, after a fifteen minute's ride I found myself in the stately silence of Walnut Park, with Caspar Leadbrooke's old-fashioned, distinctive residence scarcely half a block away. I often sought Mrs. Leadbrooke for an afternoon's half-hour, and always with a sense of pleasure in store. One never drank tea there. I detest tea, flavored with gossip and spiked with scandal. Mrs. Leadbrooke's coffee was as refreshing as her conversation, clear, mellow, and fragrant with a bit of crystalized ginger for spice and a froth of whipped cream for lightness—no hint of cloying sweetness or underlying bitterness. And with the coffee came a sort of flaky pastry, appetizing and satisfying as the rare bits of humor and philosophy which dropped from time to time in the course of her conversation.

All considered, it was with a sense of pleasurable anticipation that I touched the electric bell at the imposing entrance of the Leadbrooke home. Strangely incongruous, that bell, in contrast to the heavy oaken doors with smiling bronze Cupids, bows upraised, in bas-relief upon them, relics of past generations of high-born and affluent Caspar Leadbrookes.

Mrs. Leadbrooke admitted me—a thing unusual in itself and rendered doubly so by the fact that she was in street costume, a mannish, purple thing that became her amazingly well. Forestalling my unspoken question in a way distinctly her own, she relieved me of hat and coat and drew me into the library.

"Oh, I am glad you have come! I tried to telephone. I wouldn't have liked to go away without seeing you— I am going away, you know!" This while thrusting me into a huge, leather chair and seating herself behind the gleaming Sheraton tea-table. Pouring coffee into my favorite cup of pale Chinese porcelain, she continued to talk smoothly but with a departure from her usual manner which I was quick to detect.

"Caspar has adopted a child—a son."

My face must have portrayed my astonishment for she smiled, rather a wan smile wholly unlike her usual vivid mirthfulness. The hand holding out the amber coffee in its priceless cup shook ever so slightly.

"Indeed," said I, "I did not know Mr. Leadbrooke had any especial fondness for children."

"For children in general he hasn't," she replied. "This boy is his own."

Again my features, none too well controlled in times of stress, bespoke astonishment, this time mingled with consternation.

"I may as well tell you the story. You, of all my friends, like gossip and hearsay the least; and it is well that some one should know the truth."

Mrs. Leadbrooke's face, unusually fine and expressive, wore a stern look just now, and her slim, ringed hands toyed nervously with the loose waves of silver hair which was perhaps her greatest charm. Its soft grey that had come too early softened, enhanced, and added mystery to a face so faintly colored and so youthful that one might almost fancy the pale waves above it powdered for some "old tyme" ball.

Her pliant voice took up its story:

"It happened long ago—the boy is fourteen. Caspar was in the West, on a rest cure. You remember that he took his college course too strenuously. His father sent him west for rest, change, and what not; and there he met her." She bit into a sandwich meditatively and laid it down again.

"You've heard of Doris Greenlaw?"

I shook my head.

"No matter. Few of our friends have. She wasn't one whom he could marry, or at least he thought so, then. Youth is exceedingly foolish at best, and love makes the greatest fools of those who fancy themselves well-poised and wise."

At that moment I visualized Caspar Leadbrooke, suave, polished, immaculately correct from the top of his smooth dark head to the tips of his dull kid boots. Caspar Leadbrooke in love, reckless—

My hostess was speaking swiftly. "They were desperately in love. She had no one to warn her of rich young men, only anxious relatives who wanted her to make a match of some kind and were willing to accept risks."

Somehow I felt myself strangely in sympathy with the unknown Doris Greenlaw, lonely ward of mercenary relatives.

"And so they rode and danced and romanced the summer through . . . In the autumn Caspar came back to New Orleans."

She turned the bracelet watch on her smooth wrist, glancing at the hour. I half rose, but she waved me back with a pretty gesture.

"I was here, with Edith Terry. Edith was anxious for me to know Caspar. I was just 'out' and, as for me, I was more than anxious. The story of his infatuation had come to Edith's ears, the families were closely allied, and she had whispered it to me. I can't analyze my motive, but from that moment I wanted to find out what I could do with Caspar, to see if I could take the other girl's place in his thoughts and heart. It was only an experiment at first, a mere trying-out of my powers, but it became a desperate game and I have grown weary of the playing."

She reached for my cup and filled it with hands grown steady again.

"I was entirely eligible." She smiled, a bit scornfully. "Caspar seemed moody and despondent, but he called frequently and we went about. Frankly, I did my part. I was attracted by him, his moodiness was itself an attraction, then; and I gave him all the necessary encouragement, perhaps a little more. I was not in love with him, but I determined to make him love me and in part I succeeded. We were married in midwinter and spent a gay honeymoon in the North."

Four silver chimes, muffled by velvet portières, came delicately to our ears. She paused until the elfin echo had died away.

"There were times when he thought of Doris, even then. I knew, although she was never mentioned between us. I could charm away his blackest moods, then, and I was not afraid."

She bent her head for a moment, hands loosely folded on the polished table, and I noted once again the wonder of the dark brows and lashes beneath the whiteness of her hair.

"It was perhaps three months after our return that the letter came. We were at breakfast. . . . I shall never forget Caspar's face . . . I was wearing a turquoise gown and he had spoken pleasantly of it a moment before the mail came in. He has never spoken of my dress since, and the sight of blue makes him almost ill."

She followed the intricate pattern of a bit of ivory with a rose-tipped finger and I waited, silent. Truly the ways of the world are marvelous. The Caspar Leadbrooke's were held up as models of calm, sedate, understanding happiness.

"He left the table, the open letter beside his plate. I read it. I think he meant that I should. It was a few, nervous, jerkily written lines from Doris. A dark-haired, dark-eyed boy had been born—Doris was blue-eyed and fair—she had called him Caspar Leadbrooke Greenlaw. That was all. Not a trace of hysteria or melodrama. No reproaches, no love words. No harking back to the past. Only a mere statement of facts, granting his right to know them."

I placed my cup on the table with a decided rattle of china, wondering what was to come next and half afraid to hear.

"From that time Caspar became a stranger to me; and to himself, I think. Not a creature of moods to be charmed away and forgotten but a man suddenly awake and suffering. I think he had never before realized just what he had done. Into the crucible of life he had flung a summer's irresponsibility, reckless love, and unchecked desire—and out of it had come a dark-haired, dark-eyed boy, Caspar Leadbrooke Greenlaw."

She waited a moment, the silence tense between us. "I said that Edith and I knew of his western affair. I think we had guessed, too, the length to which it had gone. We should have helped Caspar, helped him over his ideas of caste and the petty social distinctions to which he was born and upon which he had been reared, and sent him back to happiness. Such things can be done—atmosphere, tact, friendliness—but we didn't. I wanted to see what I could do with a man whom love had once made mad. I never thought of the girl. To me, then, she was a thing apart."

The radiant afternoon sun, shining through amber hangings, suffused the room with a pale golden light. From above the walnut mantel a madonna looked down, not upon us, but at the child on her breast, and the wonder of all the universe was in her eyes. I wondered if Doris' eyes had been like that in her lonely motherhood, mystic, tender, unfathomable.

"I knew what I should do but I fought on just to keep him. I should have given him his freedom—she was more his wife than I—but I did not offer it. He could not ask. He never dreamed that I had always known I was a usurper."

It seemed strange to feel pity for Barbara Leadbrooke, she had always seemed to me so bright and capable and happy, but my heart ached for her in the pain she had borne and the pain she had yet to bear.

Her voice was tired but she held it smooth and steady, "I cannot tell you what he suffered. I have crept to his door often and often when all the house slept save him and me, to hear him murmuring as he tossed, 'Doris, Doris, Doris.' And over and over again, 'Doris, Doris, Doris.'

"And still I would not give up, living days of humiliation and nights of torment. You will think by this that I loved him, but it was not jealousy that tormented me. I was possessed by a madness to keep him, to win him again against all odds, to keep him always."

She nervously turned her sparkling rings on fingers too frail, it seemed, to carry them, and I missed the heavy luster of the wedding ring, which many generations of Leadbrooke wives had worn.

"I longed with an ardor that was almost madness for a child. A son, if miracles were yet possible; or, if such bliss could not be mine, a daughter who would bear balm in her tiny hands.

"Once, in desperation, I crept to a statue of the Virgin that was his mother's and which he keeps, veiled, in his room. I tore the veiling aside and on my knees prayed aloud for the gift of a child. I am not a Catholic, neither is Caspar, but I thought the Virgin-mother would at least pity me. Caspar chanced to find me and laughed aloud; and then I knew that he despised me."

I studied the proud small head with its silver crown, the heavy-lidded brown eyes, the graceful, purple-clad figure, and I wondered and wondered. But human beings always will be enigmas; and the Leadbrooke's, it seemed, were very human.

"In this way we have lived all of our life together. He too proud to ask and I too mad to give. He despising me and I not loving him—oh, no, I never have—but not willing to yield him to her who loved him as herself.

"Yesterday the break came. Caspar came to my room—for the first time in many months—and gave me a letter. His face was quite changed—very quiet, very gentle—and he spoke gently to me. But his eyes were new and determined.

"The letter was from Doris. She had been teaching all these years and caring for her son. She had never asked, and would not accept, a penny from Caspar— she was a thoroughbred, was Doris. And now she had contracted a fever and was ready to die. She wrote that she was sending the boy, that there was no one else to whom he could go. That was all, but it was the end for me as well as for Doris. I can no longer fight. The odds, always against me, are overwhelming now. Doris has sent her son to keep his mother's memory in his father's heart and I am an alien. I can hear Caspar walking softly, speaking gently. To him the house is full of Doris. He came upon me packing and only smiled, did not speak. I think he understands that I must go—where, don't ask me. I still have many friends."

She drew a deep breath of the perfumed air and smiled brightly at me through misty lashes.

"Good-bye, my very kind friend." I had not thought of going until she dismissed me thus gently.

"I am not wholly bad," she said, giving both her hands into mine. "Doris' boy came this morning, I'll kiss him, just once, before I go."

I murmured a wholly inadequate attempt at thanking her for her confidence, and wishing her well in her new life, passed out alone into the spacious, fragrant hall. Fumbling with hat and coat, the age-old problem of life closed in about me—so simple if its laws are obeyed to the letter, so nicely complex, if one of these laws is ignored or thrust aside. And above and about and through it all, like a silver web, the great white law of the universe—"As ye would that men should do unto you, do ye even so unto them, likewise."

A RACE FOR HONORS

BY

SUSIE A. BARDIN

—

Awarded Second Honor in 1916

A RACE FOR HONORS

THE OLD Virginia home of the Carltons, guarded by giant oaks, looked lovely and imposing in its new coat of paint. Upon this, its one hundred and twenty-fifth anniversary, it seemed ready to challenge time for another century. The spacious grounds that surrounded it were attractive and dotted here and there with numerous outer buildings all neatly designed. Charming indeed were the sights on every hand: the old-fashioned rose trellises, bird houses, rustic arbors, and, none the less attractive, the broad, dignified-looking fences running out in every direction.

The first day of October found the Carltons busy making preparations for the arrival of Miss Adelaide Van Reuck of New York, Mary Carlton's old college room-mate and chum. A letter had been received from Miss Van Reuck stating that she and her mother were en route to Florida, where the latter was to spend the winter for her health. It was Mrs. Van Reuck's plan to stop off in Richmond for a few days to visit an old friend, while Adelaide would proceed to Fredericksburg and there catch a steamer down the Rappahannock for a three days visit to Mary's home. A telegram later brought the news from Adelaide's friend and lover, Ensign Olin Milton, that he would arrive a few minutes earlier than Adelaide on the steamer from Baltimore.

All was expectancy. John Carlton, Mary's older brother, had actually staid away from his law-office and postponed urgent business in order to accompany Mary to the wharf to meet the young people. The hall clock had struck twelve, and old Aunt Liza was hurrying to have an extra fine dinner ready for the visitors. The faster she worked, the louder she sang, until Mrs. Carlton, seeing the automobile enter the upper gate, called, "Say, Aunt Liza, hadn't you better lower your voice a little, the company is coming."

Out jumped Mary and, beckoning to her parents, sweetly said: "Come Mamma and Dad and meet old Adelaide and Olin, for they are to be your adopted children."

And Mrs. Carlton added in her motherly way, "So we are your foster parents."

"How beautifully said and how very sweet of you," exclaimed Adelaide as she put her arms around the old lady's waist and drew her to her. "But just think, my adoption can't last longer than three days, for I have to get back to Richmond to pilot mother to Florida."

"Well, then," interposed Mary, "I hope you catch the Virginia contagion, which you know is a disease that causes every one who once comes to Virginia to want to come again."

"Ha, ha, ha," laughed Adelaide, "I already have the contagion—caught it from my mother, who adores Virginia, her native state."

The moment Adelaide entered the front hall, she gave an exclamation of joy as she beheld the large old-fashioned fireplace of rough stone and the great winding stairway which ascended to Mary's own room. There she spied the genuine old tester-bed and almost involuntarily found herself on the little carpeted steps leading to it.

"Oh, Olin, isn't this the quaintest place you ever saw!" she exclaimed when she joined her lover in the lower hall. "I feel that it is all a dream and I am transported somewhere back yonder to the Eighteenth Century."

"Gee, yes! The only modern thing I have seen is the automobile," replied Olin, and turning to John, he said with a merry twinkle, "How in the world did you ever consent to allow such an innovation the right of way?"

"That's what I say," quickly put in Adelaide. "I feel that an old yellow coach would be more in keeping with the spirit here."

"Ah, well," said John, "we stick pretty closely to the trodden paths, but occasionally something new will steal in. But let me tell you right now, if ever you did feel like ancient history, it will be to-morrow night, for we are planning to have a sort of historical revival of "ye olden days" and have invited a number of young people in our own community and some of the officers and soldiers from Camp Lee."

"Fine and dandy," cried Adelaide, clapping her hands.

"Yes," continued John, "we thought that just at this time, when the stress of the present war is weighing so heavily upon our minds and hearts, it would be a pleasing diversion to take a peep backward. We shall stir the ashes of the heroes of the Eighteenth Century, bring them back to life for an hour or so, startle them with the mighty issues of this world war we are facing, and show them we are dominated by the same high principles that actuated them."

"You mean that we shall impersonate Revolutionary characters?" asked Ensign Milton.

"Yes. For instance, you, Mr. Milton, will play the part of George Washington."

"And who am I to be?" asked Mary.

"And I?" followed Adelaide's eager query.

"Why, you, Miss Adelaide, are to represent Mrs. Martha Skelton; and Mary, you are to be Mrs. Custis. And I—well, I believe I shall for once aspire to the role of Thomas Jefferson. Behold the gentleman-elect!"

After a perfect feast of a dinner and a stroll down by the river's edge, all repaired to the house to bedeck themselves in their costumes. Pictures of the colonial characters were studied, their peculiar characteristics sought out, and their mode of dressing observed to the minutest details. The girls practiced the art of hair-powdering and were careful to get just the right dip to their bodices.

The next day the rooms of the grand old house were set in order and, as far as possible, every modern touch was obliterated. Chandeliers containing myriads of candles were suspended, and on the mahogany tables and mantels were placed candelabra with shades of bright colors. All the antique furniture that could be collected from the country round had been borrowed for this notable occasion. Handsome tapestry and reproductions from the masters of art adorned the walls and everything was wearing that fine air of aristocracy prevalent long years ago.

By eight o'clock the wheels of the great event were in motion and guests from far and near were arriving. Olin, as George Washington, was the first gentleman in the parlor. Here he was met by Father Carlton, representing Augustine Washington, and Mother Carlton, who played the role of Washington's mother, the once beautiful Mary Ball. And what a handsome figure was Olin! His wig was silvery white, and his face, free from all powder and paint, was extraordinarily handsome in its full flush of health. His costume was an array of gorgeous velvet. Gold buckles adorned his neat pumps, about his neck was clustered lace, and lace of the same rich kind fell gracefully from the ends of his sleeves, half hiding his hands and allowing only the tapering ends of his fingers to be seen.

A great deal of wholesome fun was occasioned by attempts to guess the different characters as they entered. But almost every one clamored forth "Thomas Jefferson!" when John Carlton entered, for he carried out to the minutest detail his style of dress. Being tall and thin with ruddy cheeks, he could well impersonate Jefferson. His face wreathed in smiles, he entered the parlor with a graceful gliding step, carrying in his right hand that characteristic old quill pen.

As he approached Washington he gave a profound bow, full of the grace that Jefferson himself would have put into it. Olin was so impressed by the striking resemblance to photographs of the original that he murmured almost unconsciously, "Jefferson still survives,"—and this remark brought forth a roar of applause.

Next entered a long string of boys: Patrick Henry, Samuel Adams, Richard Henry Lee, John Hancock, Richard Montgomery, Payton Randolph, and, among many others, young Alexander Hamilton and old Dr. Benjamin Franklin.

All awaited with eager expectancy the arrival of the colonial maids and dames, and, when they did appear, it took deep thinking to guess who they were. The first lady to enter was Mrs. Martha Custis, a beautiful widow in her twenties. As we know, she was represented by Mary Carlton, who was well suited to the character, having such regular features, chestnut brown hair, and even the hazel eyes. The moment Washington espied her coming, he advanced to meet her, took her hand, and led her away to introduce her to his distinguished friends.

Next came Adelaide, impersonating Mrs. Martha Skelton, and looking even more beautiful in her historical regalia than in her modern day costume. She was gorgeously robed in delicate pink taffeta almost completely covered with airy white chiffon. Gatherings of lace completed the bodice which was cut low in front, disclosing a perfect neck adorned with an old-fashioned chain and cross. Her hair was parted slightly, with two long curls falling from each side and hanging gracefully over the front of her shoulders.

Exclamations came from the on-lookers as this dream of beauty entered. No sooner had Thomas Jefferson caught sight of her than, with all the grace of a dancing master, he rushed to meet her and they soon drifted apart from the rest for a private chat.

In the meanwhile the room was fairly crowded with girls. There was Miss Randolph, Miss Dandridge, Miss Lucy Flucker, Miss Dorothy Quincy, Miss Mary Willis Ambler, Miss Schuyler of New York, and many, many others of Revolutionary days.

Adelaide, as she beheld all this sea of faces, turned to John: "This is the most inspiring scene I've ever witnessed. I only wish my mother were here to see all these old time lads and lassies. How she would appreciate it all."

"No doubt her eyes would dwell longest on her own daughter," unhesitatingly declared John. "And believe me, if the original Mrs. Skelton could behold her representative to-night, her heart would swell with pride."

The tide of John's love was at its flood and Adelaide saw that it was liable to rush him into hasty declarations, so she tried to use policy lest her answers might be an impetus to drive him onward.

Recovering from so perfect a compliment, she merrily replied: "Thank you, John; if that be the case, I had better remain Mrs. Martha Skelton forever and for aye."

"No," came his emphatic answer, "for if I were to remain Thomas Jefferson you would surely have to change your name. The Fates decreed that, you remember."

Poor Adelaide with all her strategy and cunning felt that she was whipped at her own game. The castle was stormed! Where was the exit? Bewildered, she sought refuge in the feeble question:

"Why, how was that, John?"

"Well, she married Jefferson, and I would that Fate would decree such happiness for me."

"Oh, History! History! the bane of my existence," thought Adelaide, "it was the bug-bear of all my days at school and it is even trying to torment me now."

She picked up the dainty handkerchief lying in her lap, involuntarily carried it to her mouth, and began vigorously to wipe two rosy lips. John, who saw he was in the crisis of the battle, renewed his courage and hope, and broke the silence:

"Adelaide, I'm ashamed of myself for saying it when I know that my honored friend Washington possesses your heart. He deserves all the happiness that Heaven and earth can bestow; but, Adelaide, I'm profoundly in love with you!"

Excitedly she brought into play that little instrument of coquetry, a tiny suggestion of a fan, and, placing it over her eyes, steathily glanced at John while she nervously asked:

"Do you think it is genuine love, John? Can love be born so quickly?"

With all the dignity of the character he was portraying, he looked her straight in the face as he said, "Yes, love can be born in an hour, nay, in a minute. It sits enthroned in the heart from the beginning of life and it only needs the sight of the right person to awaken it to consciousness. Such has been my experience. You surely can not blame me, but you can pity me. But why pity me? Someone has well said, 'Nothing but infinite pity is sufficient for the infinite pathos of human life'."

"Do, pray, hush, John," she cried. "You talk as if you were doomed to die in an electric chair, or possibly you think you are making a great speech to save the life of a criminal. Listen, the real Jefferson brought honor and fame to Mrs. Skelton. What have you to offer me?"

"Nothing but myself, a plain country lawyer. What honor would you have me bring you?"

"Why, the honor of being a Congressman's wife. Why on earth did you lose out in the last primary and deprive me of that honor?"

"Because the low-down, common element in the majority was against me. Would you marry me if I had been elected?"

"Possibly so."—She paused, once again at her ease.

"Can Washington yonder supply the desired honors?"

"Well, he has the prospect of soon being promoted to the rank of Lieutenant—and then up the ladder he'll climb."

"Then, my Congressional misfortune means the loss of a wife!" murmured John, his voice modulated to a minor strain.

But quicker than a flash as if possessed by the spirit of the man he was impersonating and imbued with Jefferson's determination, he rallied to ask:

"Suppose I yet win—what then?"

Adelaide sat a moment in serious contemplation. Suddenly as if she had hit upon a wise decision, she replied:

"Then, John, I'll make you this proposition: let it be a race for honors between Jefferson and Washington, and whichever one reaches the goal first, I'll marry."

"Good! Amen and Amen!" he almost shouted.

At this moment a great volley of voices interrupted, "Speech, Mr. Washington, speech."

Olin, who had been deeply engaged in conversation with Mary, was overcome by embarrassment and his tongue almost refused to work. A voice from the further end of the room called out:

"Sit down, Mr. Washington, your modesty equals your valor."

Washington gave a dignified bow.

"My friends," he said, "I scarcely know what topic to discuss. You remember it was Washington's rule 'to speak seldom but on important subjects'."

"Then, Woman's Suffrage," suggested Miss Schuyler of New York.

"No, please don't," cried Mary, "that would disturb the peace of our illustrious dead."

"Preparedness," came the next suggestion.

"Good," declared Olin. "Then the most forceful speech I can make is to point out to you my own distressing condition right now—the result of *unpreparedness.*"

The crowd roared with laughter and cries of "Vive le Washington" were heard on all sides.

At that moment a musical voice from the far end of the room was heard to say: "Well, if Washington will not speak, then let him give way to Woodrow Wilson who will tell us how to make the world safe for democracy."

To the surprise of all in filed a group of gentlemen impersonating Wilson, McAdoo, Baker, General Pershing and several others. Such shouts and screams of delight as followed! Wilson advanced to greet Washington and with that characteristic smile playing over his face, calmly said: "Thrice honored are we, the gentlemen of the Twentieth Century, to enter this hall of fame and greet in person you eminent gentlemen of the past—" Here the greeting was interrupted by the suggestion: "Give Mr. Washington a short summary of the events of the hour."

Mr. Wilson accepted the suggestion and they entered upon a discussion of the times that *were* and the times that *are*. And so the hours sped to twelve o'clock when the Eighteenth Century vanished again into the past with the goodbyes of the departing guests.

[31]

Late rising the next morning put the entire Carlton family in a rush to get Olin and Adelaide off to meet the steamer, and just two minutes before the boat left the dock the two were standing on the upper deck waving good-bye. Adelaide's last words were heard across the water: "John, run with patience the race that is set before you." A wave of his hand was the response.

John lost no time in beginning the race and that very afternoon started to set his wires. He realized that the first step was to enlist the interest of old Sim Jackson, the Democratic boss and the greatest croaker in the swamp of political pollution. Like a powerful dynamo operated by the mechanism of chicanery and subterfuge, all he had to do was to remain in his headquarters in the center of the Congressional district and shoot out a current of messages and letters. The effect could be felt in every county and precinct.

John further knew that Mannering Doyle was a personal enemy of old man Sim and that his nomination on the Democratic ticket had so inflated Jackson with fury that he would do almost anything to bring about Doyle's defeat.

"Now," thought John, "let me get him entangled in this net, and the spicy odor of contention will be strong."

That afternoon, spurred on by a strong hope, he approached the old gentleman and, feeling his way along cautiously inch by inch, finally came out with the question:

"Say, Mr. Jackson, what do you think of my running for Congress on an Independent ticket?"

Mr. Jackson's red flabby face seemed to swell with enthusiasm, and cramming his hands down in his coat-pockets as if trying to reach the depth of an abyss, he blurted out:

"Well, I be-ding, if I wasn't thinking about that very thing this morning. Carlton, you're a trump!" And, so saying, he dealt him a good-natured blow on his broad shoulders. Then he continued: "Get to work, my boy, I'm with you. I have a little money left and my influence is as good as ever. But, say, Carlton, before you announce yourself, let me get about a little and kind-a, you know, put my finger on the pulse of the public. Then, if the symptoms are good you can just stand off and see the thing buzz!" and the old man chuckled exultingly.

"Well then, Mr. Jackson, I'm going to depend on you; and when you are ready for my card to appear, just give me the signal."

"All right," acquiesced the old man, and as Carlton walked away he heard old Sim muttering, "Be-ding, if I don't admire his independence. He's a chip of the old block."

And something within whispered to John, "Yes, and so did Jefferson like independence." But he smothered that wee voice lest some one might read his mind.

Such a stack of letters as John took to the postoffice the next morning, urgent appeals to all the influential men in the surrounding counties. In a few days replies came bringing promise of support should he decide to run, while some urged his candidacy giving wise suggestions as to the best methods for his campaign. Every word written and spoken was welcomed.

On Monday of the second week, John hastened to old man Sim's office. "Good morning, Mr. Jackson," he said in a happy tone, "Good or bad news?"

"Good," blurted Jackson, aiming a stream of tobacco juice at the nearby spittoon. "Put your card in the paper and be-ding if this isn't going to be a lively chase. Why, son, the field is ripe. And think, just thirty more days before the harvest! Get to work!"

The next day John's card in glaring type met the eyes of every one, and the buzz had surely started.

A lucky thing happened that very day. He received an invitation to speak before The Farmer's Union Association and of course gladly accepted. A great concourse from every section of his district was there and it proved the finest of opportunities to air politics. John gave free rein to his eloquence and in an hour's time had more converts than a few. Groups of typical clod-hoppers put their heads together and decided, "That's the kind o' man we fellahs want to go up yander to Washington to speak our wishes. We'll vote for him sure."

Meanwhile the haughty Mannering Doyle stalked about preaching death and destruction to John's hopes.

"Poor fool," he was heard to say, "without the ghost of a chance—and he hasn't sense enough to know it."

The days sped on, the political thermometer rising higher and higher until the Democratic nominee and the Independent candidate were sweltering in white heat. Every newspaper in the district carried double-headers concerning the hot Congressional campaign. Never before had the political pot in this district reached such a mighty stage of ebullition.

November fourth found each candidate's forces well organized and ready for a strenuous day at the polls. If one could only get a bird's eye view of the voting territory, what a panorama of interesting pictures would unfold. Here come the rural voters manfully trudging in to be met by a galaxy of politicians, electioneers and grafters, whispering airy promises. The different chairmen of the executive committees sit awaiting replies to inquiries. And old Sim Jackson upon his throne by the spittoon is keeping watch over the entire field.

Through the hours of ten and eleven telegraphic reports showed the old man that the prospects for the Independent candidate were bright. But lo! the hour of twelve brought the news that Carlton was rapidly losing ground to the regular nominee, who now seemed to be the strongest candidate in the field. Mannering Doyle's election at this early forecast seemed assured.

In great suspense, Carlton rushed to Mr. Jackson's private office and reaching the door, touched it furtively, just enough for him to catch a picture of old man Sim supporting his head with his right hand and unconsciously folding his lower lip with his right.

"The jig is up with me," thought John. "That very look of Jackson's is a prophecy of defeat."

Without another moment's hesitation, he bolted through the door and throwing himself despairingly in the nearest chair, panted:

"My prospects have reached the wall, haven't they?"

Out blabbed Jackson, "Be-ding if they haven't. Doyle is far ahead of every one in the field." And, so saying, he jumped to his feet, rushed his fingers through his hair until he had it standing upright, and paced the room in a perfect frenzy, muttering indistinctly.

The hitherto proud, chivalrous John was sinking lower and lower into the depths of desperation when the old man as if by sudden impulse exclaimed:

"Pshaw, Carlton, that won't do, sit up, be a man. Just remember that Sim Jackson still has some hope left. His trump card, boy, is still in his hand and it's going to be played pretty soon. Get back to your den and await results. It won't be well for you to be seen about here too much."

As soon as the door closed behind John, Sim began to review the situation: "Poor John! I know as things now stand he is sure to be defeated, for indications from all parts of the district show that Doyle is winning by leaps and bounds. It must not be! I must reverse the course of things. Be-ding if I don't. Run a bluff—yes, that's my trump card."

So saying he reached for his telegraph pad and quicker than a flash wrote these words:

"Republican candidate running far ahead. Independent candidate next in the lead. By all means turn every bit of Democratic strength to Independent or the Democrats lose this Congressional District."

Copies of the above were addressed to the chairman of each local Democratic Committee in the district.

Grabbing up his old slouch hat, Jackson rushed out, trusting no one but himself to bear these important messages to the telegraph operator, at whose side he stood until the last word of every message was clicked off. Then back to his spittoon he betook himself to sit and wait.

At four o'clock a messenger-boy arrived with the following telegram:

"INDEPENDENT GAINING SOME GROUND. REPUBLICAN CANDIDATE PRACTICALLY ELIMINATED. WILL FURTHER ADVISE WITHIN AN HOUR.

A. J. PHILIPS."

Old Sim chuckled.

Four fifteen, another message, reading:

"INDEPENDENT AND REGULAR NOMINEE ABOUT EVEN.

OSCAR McKAY."

Only low murmurings escaped old Sim's lips.

Four thirty-five, still another message:

"SINCE RECEIPT OF YOURS, STRENGTH HAS PRACTI-CALLY ALL BEEN TURNED TO INDEPENDENT.

JOS. E. VICKERS."

Others in similar vein followed from the committee-men.

Old Sim threw the last of the telegrams to the table and began soliloquizing:

"Pshaw, Sim Jackson hasn't given all his years to politics for nothing. Be-ding if I don't know every crook and turn in this old game. It will take more than a Mannering Doyle to stump me. Great Caesar! I wonder if he will ever get out of the ditch I'm going to put him in. He'll know by midnight that he can't quietly double-cross me as he did last year! My time has come."

How old Sim did squint his muddy blue eyes, sneer and gloat over his prospective victory!

Messages continued to pour in from all quarters until a late hour, and these kept Jackson's encouragement rising and falling until the final batch brought the flood-tide of joy: "Independent wins by safe majority."

"Humph! It's just like I expected. It takes Sim Jackson to do the thing," muttered the old man as he leisurely walked to the phone:

"Hello, Carlton, it's all right, my boy. You are elected by a safe majority."

"Say, Mr. Jackson, just hold the phone and listen to my cheers."—And such a blast as followed!

"Oh," thought John, "I'm fixed now—a seat in Congress—with Mrs. Martha Skelton as my bride. Jefferson, Jefferson, I wonder if you ever were as happy as I am to-night!"

John waited the greater part of the next day until the returns were all in and then flashed this message over the wires to Adelaide:

"ELECTED TO CONGRESS ON INDEPENDENT TICKET. JEFFERSON CLAIMS HIS OWN."

Adelaide was in Norfolk, where she had gone to take leave of Ensign Milton, whose ship was liable to start at any moment for a French port. With several friends she was stopping at a fashionable hotel in the city. On this particular evening she was adorned in all her festal glory and looked a princess in this glittering realm of wealth, beauty, chivalry, and fashion. Her lover's popularity among his polished circle of friends had brought her the homage she so much courted, and she was supremely happy. The orchestra was just beginning to flood the scene with music when Carlton's telegram was put into Adelaide's hands. She drifted a wee bit back from the merry circle and took her seat upon a vacant settee nearby. Olin soon followed and, as he approached, Adelaide declared excitedly:

"Well, Olin, Jefferson still survives with all his passion for Independence. Elected to Congress, mind you, on an Independent ticket! Is it possible that the pen is mightier than the sword?"

"To be sure not," came Olin's only response.

Adelaide with a most pitiable expression, looked up into Olin's handsome, honest face, and with a sad note in her voice said:

"He has won the victory, Olin, and I am caught in my own net."

"Never, never, so long as Washington lives," declared Olin with an air of triumph as he fell in the seat beside her. "Just remember, little girl, Washington was first in all things—in war, in peace, in the hearts of his countrymen. Surely now he must be *first* in the heart of his lady-love."

"But you see, Olin, you are not first in the race for honors," added Adelaide, great anxiety expressed in her tone.

"Well, then read this letter and be convinced that just one week ago I received official notice of my promotion to the rank of Lieutenant."

LAND OF DREAMS

BY

ZOE KINCAID BROCKMAN

Awarded Third Honor in 1916

LAND OF DREAMS

It seems a thousand years ago—and it was twenty,
    maybe,
And what now seems a fairy isle was but a simple
    farm;
But, oh, the rose-lit rapture, when in dreaming I
    remember
The way the huddled maples held the old house close
    and warm.

There were doves around the eaves, and cattle on the
    hillside,
And little lambs that nuzzled in the fragrant clover
    fields,
I remember how we watched them in the purple light,
    together—
Strange what a plenteous harvest each deep-sown
    memory yields!

And then the long, brown, winding road, and you were
    gone—so swiftly,
It seemed the night had settled, though the sun was
    golden-bright;
And I have cried your name aloud—how foolish Youth
    can suffer!—
When all was still and silent with the kindly drug of
    night.

It seems a thousand years ago—and it was twenty, maybe,
A deathly, deep tranquility of slow years has been born;
But, oh, dear Brushwood Boy of mine, I ask: "Do you remember
The way the sunset deepened on the gilded rows of corn?"

AT THE END OF THE WAY

BY

MARY C. ROBINSON

Awarded First Honor in 1917

AT THE END OF THE WAY

"When the little ol' owl comes a-hootin' in the night,
Pull up the kivers and snuggle down tight!
Fo', chil'uns, when yo' heah dat little owl cry,
Jes' as sure as breathin' some one's gwine to die.
So t'ink of yo' sins an' be keerful what yo' do,
'Cause maybe dat little ol' owl means you."

When I was a youngster and heard the owl cry,
'Neath the thick covers trembling I'd lie;
I'd think of Mammy Ca'line's fearsome tale,
And shiver like a leaf in a wintry gale.
O, the little old owl in the sweet-gum tree,
I hoped and I prayed that he didn't mean me!

It's many a winter and summer and fall,
Since Ca'line answered the little owl's call;
Most all her "white folks" have fallen asleep,
Lonely and alone my watch I keep,
Hark—the mournful note in the sweet-gum tree—
O, I hope that little old owl means me.*

* Not long after receiving the award of the Federation Mrs. Robinson came to the "End of the Way."

[47]

THE APOTHEOSIS

BY

HELEN ELLWANGER HANFORD

———

Awarded First Honor in 1917

THE APOTHEOSIS*

I T WAS a day late in March and Dr. Wharfield was starting out for his afternoon walk. His daughter standing at the door bade him farewell and suggested a heavier overcoat. "And don't walk too far," she added tenderly. He turned away to hide the feeling of vexation which it seemed absolutely out of his power to control. Not for worlds would he have let her know that her gentle solicitude made him feel as helpless as a child sent off to school alone for the first time or a timid old woman making her trip to town. All this he must learn to accept—he would learn—but what a day it had been, what a day! The late breakfast, the silly hour of puttering in the garden, examining his plants for he knew not what, the period of rest before and after lunch, and now the afternoon walk on which nothing depended and which therefore lost all zest.

Unconsciously his steps turned to the church where for thirty years he had preached. As he walked along, a little heavily, he met an aged friend in his wheeled chair. He was lying back, enjoying the brief sunshine and looking about him with mild interest—an old, old man, content with life. Wharfield greeted him and then with the quavering voice still in his ears, started at the cheerful calling of his own name. He found that he was passing the house of Mr. Corsen, his suc-

* Printed by permission of *Holland's Magazine,* Dallas, Texas.

cessor, and Corsen hurrying out brought him back into the study. The room was full of signs of work: the table was strewn with books and papers; other books were lying about on the chairs. Corsen swept them aside with hospitable hand. He owned to being busy but then he liked that. "Didn't you, sir?"

Wharfield managed to hide his shudder at the past tense and smiled an affirmative answer. It was quite true. He had indeed liked being busy. He had liked it with the whole force of his nature up to the very day six months ago when he had found himself suddenly, irrevocably cut off from his work. Again as so often he wondered whether failure would not have been easier to bear.

With an effort he brought himself back to Corsen and his affairs. They were the usual problems of the young preacher, the effort to reconcile religion and science, complicated by the desire to be true to himself and still not to offend his brothers. "Easter sermons always bother me a little," he confessed. "How can one prove anything at all there? And this is an age of reason. But I've got three more weeks for that."

He looked young and a little pitiful to Dr. Wharfield. He was so far as yet from the place where he could see clearly the things that count. But oh, the glory of his young strength! Drawn on by the older man's interest he outlined his sermon for the next Sunday. It was finely conceived and Dr. Wharfield forgot himself for the moment as he watched the young man's glowing face. "Do you think that will get them, sir?"

he asked boyishly. Dr. Wharfield was very sure it would get them. He stood for a moment with his hand on Corsen's shoulder and then, leaving him to work it out at white heat, went home and sought his own study.

He would have been blind if he had not been struck instantly and poignantly by the contrast it presented to the room he had just left. Here was no confusion nor the need of any. His books looked down on him from the four sides of the room and every one was in its proper place. Had the same hand that had transformed his life touched them too? They looked alien, almost as if they slept and were waiting for another to come and bring them back to consciousness. He remembered the days when work done faithfully had brought him as reward an evening of poetry. He was passionately fond of verse, for oddly mixed with the mental vigor which was peculiarly his was another strain, something gentle and reflective of which few knew even the existence. Well, the time for reading had come. The rest of the day was his and the whole next day and the next. They stretched in an endless procession before him—*days to be used*.

He shivered and threw out his open hands in an impotent gesture. As he did so, he touched a book on the table, a volume of Sophocles unopened for months, and at the touch memory played a curious trick and words heard a year before and since forgotten leaped to his consciousness. Sam Harrison, his physician and old friend, had found him absorbed in his reading and had suggested half quizzically that he write a book on some phase of the Greek drama. "I'll bet you know your Æschylus as well as you do the Old Testament," Harrison had said. He remembered how he had smiled and replied that the *magnum opus* must wait till he was an old man. "My sermons take all the writing power that's in me now," he had added ruefully. It was true: he had always lacked facility in expressing his thoughts and many hours had been spent in polishing what came to him roughhewn into masterpieces of literary expression. Now—he was an old man. The pitying eyes of his friends told him that every day. And the lack of time was scarcely an obstacle! He tried to be ironical but in spite of himself his pulses quickened. Was all indeed lost? Surely not if here in his quiet study he might work serenely on a great task, less spurred to be sure by the thought of immediate use for what lay under his hand, but with as fine a purpose. He pushed back the heavy hair from his forehead with the gesture that bespoke intense thought and began his work. At first it was exhilarating; then he lost himself in it too completely to be conscious of any feeling. The need for light brought him back to himself two hours later and as he went to turn it on, he staggered. His head felt curiously dizzy; a blackness came before him—

He was thankful afterward that it was Harrison that found him and not his daughter. He was spared her self-reproaches and he was able to get at the truth at once. It was what he might have known; it was indeed little more than a repetition of what he had been told half a year before—a truth too stupendous to be grasped at once: he must do no absorbing work of any kind, physical or mental. The tenseness of the last two hours had been as bad for him in its way as mountain climbing. He must save himself day by day and every day. An infringement of rules, and he might go out like a flash at any moment. If he were careful, very careful, he might live many years. And with the words, "many years," Harrison looked away, his face drawn with pity. To Wharfield it was as if the other had taken the remaining pages of his life, torn off as they were, and crumpled them up before his eyes. Unconsciously he moved his head from side to side like some distracted animal in captivity. He was sending up wordless, incoherent prayers. But God seemed not to hear him.

* * * * * *

It was Easter Sunday three weeks later. To Dr. Wharfield the time had seemed as many years, filled to the brim with idleness. He had dreaded this day especially, but to his amazement he awoke with a feeling of tremulous gladness. It was in every breath that he drew, in the faint sweet smells of spring, in his daughter's loving greeting. Intangible, it eluded all analysis, but, wonderfully, it was there, quivering in his whole being, and it did not leave him as the early morning hours passed. His hands trembled as he dressed for church.

He started off alone half an hour before the time of the service and as he walked along he rejoiced in the faces of children and in the sunlight shining through the trees. Entering the great flower-filled church, he went softly to the family pew and bowed his head for a moment in prayer, but no words came, only that surging sense of joy. He leaned back with closed eyes . . . Presently old memories began to stir. If words could live, the winged things, how many words of his would flutter about him now. Here he had laid his hands on little children and blessed them, here he had spoken the sacred words of the marriage service and the solemn requiem for the dead, and here every spring for thirty years he had reminded men of the resurrection of Christ. . . .

Far off, the choir was practising the morning music. It floated to him, triumphant, ecstatic, and mysteriously it seemed to him as if all the Easters he had ever known were merged into one and were blending their music with that of the anthem. Again that overpowering sense of joy; but more intensified now, more tangible —a thing about to be interpreted. He waited spellbound. And then slowly, from somewhere far away, a great flood of feeling rolled nearer and nearer and passed over him. Rather, he felt himself carried along with it to another world. . . . The last notes died away and he sat shaken and weak but elated beyond the power of words to express: for as surely as he knew that he possessed a mortal body, he knew that his soul was immortal. He knew it with the calm of experience; he knew it as one knows the axioms of mathematics.

His daughter came in and sat beside him and he started and looked around. The church was filling rapidly. The organist had begun to play; but the pulpit was empty. A little later he noticed Dr. Harrison talking earnestly to a group of men at the rear of the church, and rising quietly he made his way to them. There was reason enough for commotion. Mr. Corsen had suddenly been taken sick and was unable to come to the church. Meanwhile the congregation waited. Harrison turned to the minister who was to assist at the service. So did the others of the little group, and he in turn, sermonless and agonized, looked at Dr. Wharfield. No one spoke.

Dr. Wharfield smiled. "Yes," he said, "I will speak to them."

Dr. Harrison started forward, words of protest on his lips. The eyes of the two old friends met. In the look of one was utter unconsciousness of all save his God-given opportunity and when the physician of the body saw that radiance, the words he would have spoken remained unuttered.

Through the responses and the prayers, Dr. Wharfield sat silent, his head lifted high. He was not thinking consciously. He had not the faintest idea what he was about to say or the faintest curiosity concerning it. Over and over he was repeating the words, "I am the resurrection and the life." He had heard them in the reading of the Scriptures, and again they faced him in the beautiful memorial window to his wife. They blended with his mood, beating in his pulses, rising and falling with his breathing.

There was a pause. The assisting minister gave a word of explanation: "Mr. Corsen had been detained; Dr. Wharfield was to preach the morning sermon"— an old man. "My sermons take all the writing power

"My friends," he began. His voice, unused to filling the space of the church, sounded weak; he felt for his breath control. "My dear friends, I bring you a message this Easter morning in the words of our Lord, 'I am the resurrection, and the life'."

There had been a little stir as he rose to speak but at his first words a deep hush fell. Was it the strange magnetic quality in his voice or that divine assurance that possessed him? They leaned forward to his words, listening as they had never listened before, and yet later none could tell what he said for to no two was the message the same. It was as if he gave utterance to the secretest emotions of the heart, those vague strugglings which men feel and recognize as the presence of God. Tenderly his words fell, words which so naturally and exquisitely clothed the feeling that pervaded him that they seemed a part of it, not to be separated from it. And as he spoke, limits of time and space vanished and all became one great present: Jesus of Nazareth, loved ones that death had taken—they were no longer remote; they were close at hand, living, and joyous. Men and women wept, but their tears were without bitterness for the sting of death was gone.

Had he spoken ten minutes or an hour? They could not have told, but his message was given. "Cast your reason from you," he pleaded. "Yield to that which is higher than any reason, O, dear children of God." A ray of sunlight fell upon his face and the slender vase of lilies beside him. The one showed as white and pure as the other. "Look into the faces of the flowers; gaze through the eyes of your spirit upon the faces of your beloved dead. And then listen to the words of Jesus, 'I am the resurrection,'"—his voice faltered—"'and—the—life.'"

So gently he sank back that for a moment, their eyes blinded by tears, they sat motionless. Dr. Harrison was the first to reach him and feel for the heart beat. He straightened himself in a moment and looked at the others and in his face was no grief but a great joy that God had spared His servant the long bondage of the empty years. Still no one moved or spoke and then in the silence—the notes of the great organ pealed forth jubilantly and the voices of the choir rose in a rapturous chorus.

THE MESSAGE OF THE TUSCANIA
BY
ZOE KINCAID BROCKMAN

Awarded First Honor in 1918

THE MESSAGE OF THE TUSCANIA*

IN THE interest of war gardens for the children of the industrial sections of my community, I, as one of a committee from my Woman's Club, was distributing vegetable and flower seeds from house to house. The day, though crisp and cool, was full of tantalizing suggestions of spring. From the neighboring open country came the faint, pleasing smell of freshly turned earth. The small clean porches and tidy yards of the mill village blossomed with eager, romping children. Sashes were raised and limp, clean curtains billowed to and fro. Everywhere the proffered seeds were smilingly received and soaring plans for fruitful gardens and gay flower-beds poured eagerly into my ears.

Around the door and at the open windows of a white-painted wooden building which had been used as a school house before the opening of a more commodious brick structure I saw chatting groups of women and girls and crossed to ask their coöperation in the work I was doing among them.

Upon entering the building, I saw that a demonstration of some kind was in progress. Several women were grouped about a four-burner oil stove, looking interestedly at the contents of an oblong pan which a tall, stooped woman in starched grey gingham had just

---

* In 1918 the contestants were limited to the subject "How One Woman Helped Uncle Sam Win the War." When this story was published in *Everywoman's Magazine* in July of that year the title was changed.

removed from the oven. The room was bare and clean, containing, besides the oil stove, a home-made kitchen cabinet, a small zinc-topped table and a half dozen rush-bottomed chairs. Several benches were ranged along the wall. Curtains of unbleached muslin hung at each of the six windows.

I was pleasantly greeted as I joined the group around the stove. Evidently they were accustomed to seeing strange faces among them. The contents of the pan were being deftly turned out upon a square of fringed muslin spread across the table. It proved to be corn muffin, deliciously odorous, delicately browned. I sniffed delightedly and exclaimed with the others over its crusty perfection. The woman in grey gingham explained that when eaten hot it must be broken, never cut. She proceeded to break it swiftly into small, uneven squares which she offered to us, together with small pats of butter, on thick white saucers. Evidently a lesson as to the mixing and baking of the bread had gone before. I was sorry to have missed any part of this most delightful demonstration, and, after eating my portion of the golden bread of the South, I determined to add this recipe to the many others gathered from time to time. Also, I was eager to learn the nature of the little gathering upon which I had stumbled.

When the others had scattered after having washed dishes and pans in a blue enameled dish-pan and emptied the water carefully over a small sunny garden in the rear, I introduced myself to the tall woman in grey, who was, as I had surmised, a leader among them. I explained my mission in the village and why I had so unceremoniously answered the call of her open door.

She gave me a slow smile before speaking and in it was complete understanding and a gracious welcome.

"I am glad to have you come in." She did not speak with ease. Her plain, worn face was flushed and she swallowed nervously. "This place belongs to the village, not to me."

"Won't you tell me about it?" I asked. I felt an eager desire to know what had brought those interested, questioning groups around this shy, stooped woman in the big bright room with its polished stove and well-filled cabinet.

I motioned her to sit, as if I were the hostess and she the guest. She spread her stiff white apron smoothly across her long knees. Her fingers went nervously to a huge oval brooch at her throat. It was the sort of pin one often sees worn by women of a past generation, cherishing within an oval of glass a twist of hair or a pictured face. This one contained neither picture nor hair, but a much tarnished brass military button against a background of stained khaki.

"I had a son, just one. He was on his way to France and perished with the *Tuscania.*" Her yellowed, wrinkled hands lay passive, her voice held a singularly quiet note.

I did not speak. I did not wish to interrupt the trend of her thought. I had asked a simple, almost an idle question. I had not expected such a confidence as this.

"He was a beautiful boy, just twenty-two, big, and strong, and good." I thought again how wonderful it is that somehow, to mothers, their sons are always beautiful, and strong, and good.

"His body was washed up on the Irish coast, so torn and bruised that no one recognized him, but he was one of the few whose identification tags had been stamped. One of his comrades clipped this piece of cloth and button from his coat and sent it to me. He said in his letter that a boy's mother was always the one of whom he talked to his comrades in the lonely, blue times that come to a soldier, and that he'd often and often heard my boy speak lovingly of me."

She spoke so quietly that I knew the storm of her grief was spent, but her hand went again and again to the pin with its blackened khaki and tarnished, wave-battered button in the same loving gesture that a mother uses when she lays a caressing hand upon the head of her child.

"When I had the news that he had gone—that way, I felt as if I would go mad." It was heart breaking, the pathos in the words "that way." My eyes filled with ready tears, but the faded eyes opposite me were calm and dry.

"Of my big, handsome boy I had only a blackened button and a bit of cloth left me. I laid them on the table before me one night, and I thought and thought. There was no blood stain on the frayed bit of the uniform that had been so stiff and new when my son went away from me. He had not died fighting as he would have wished to do. They hadn't the opportunity to fight—those boys. The button and cloth were stained by the black waters of the ocean through which his helpless body had been swept."

As she spoke her figure took on a new dignity, her voice had a martial ring. She no longer looked old and stooped and thin. The spirit of Spartan mothers shone in her eyes.

"My boy was willing and eager to fight for his country, but he hadn't the chance. He had been murdered in the foulest kind of way. Now, I asked myself, what are you going to do about it?

"I had been working for the Red Cross ever since the war began—knitting a little, sewing a little, going to the workroom sometimes. But all in a careless sort of way—I know now it was careless, I thought then that it was enough. My eyesight is poor and there was much at home to do, and somehow, even with my only son in a training camp, I didn't just see it right, then. "But," she leaned toward me, her plain face glorified, "that piece of cloth stained by the salt water of the Atlantic and that button scarred and dented by the rocks against which my boy's body had been dashed, spoke to me louder and more clearly than the sight of his living, breathing, uniformed body had ever done. I was working and praying before and I was saving and stinting in my kitchen, but I wasn't fighting then. I'm fighting now. That's what my boy was going across to do. I know his last thought was the regretful one that his work was left for others to do. Well, he was wrapped in canvas and buried on a rocky foreign sea-coast, but he isn't gone and he never will be gone. He's living and fighting every day through me, his mother. What are mothers made for, if not to work, and pray, and fight for their sons?

"And with my son gone from me, there are thousands and thousands of other women's boys for whom I can pray and work and with whom I can fight. I had this scrap of cloth and battered button made into a pin and to me it means 'The Order of Mothers Who Fight at Home'."

I looked about the long, bare room, so clean and orderly and bright, and knew that I was going to learn its history.

"I kept on going to the work-room and knitting at night, but I couldn't do much of that sort of work and I wasn't satisfied. I wanted to fight with every ounce of my strength. My boy was calling to me, and I wanted to make my efforts count.

"On every hand I heard 'food conservation' and 'economy in the kitchen.' I knew I could cook—the good, plain cooking that my generation was taught. I knew there were women who could not, who did not know how to save as the government is calling on us to do now. I wanted to teach them. You know they say that food will win the war.

"I heard of this building and asked the mill management for the use of it. I explained why I wanted it and they gave it gladly. So many of their women work, so many marry young before they know anything domestic. I wanted to teach the girls and women to make cornbread, to cook peas and beans, rice and cereals as they should be cooked; to give their families wholesome, nourishing food and not just fried meats and baking powder biscuit. There's a food conservation card in every window now." She smiled in pardonable pride. I had noticed the food pledges, the rosy children. How wonderful the one scarred button had been!

"I took my boy's last pay check and fitted out this room. The girls made the curtains at my home of cloth woven at the mill in which they are employed. They were glad of an opportunity to learn these things. They wanted to save, to use the prescribed foods, to do just as the government asked them to do, but they didn't know how. I'm teaching them what I know, and we're learning the new things together."

She stopped suddenly and became almost self-conscious again. Two small girls strolled by plying long amber needles from which dangled webs of grey yarn. They waved smilingly to my companion and received from her a motherly smile in return.

"Do you have knitting classes, also?" I asked. She smiled rather shyly.

"I haven't any 'classes' at all. I come here for a part of every day, and the women and girls come in as they can. Sometimes I bring a bit of knitting and there's always some one who wants to learn. I teach the girls to knit and depend on their young eyes to do what my failing sight almost forbids me to do."

"Do you furnish your cooking materials also?" I did not wish to be impertinent, but I was eager to know more of what seemed such a friendly, helpful plan.

"We all help about that." The tone in which she said "we" was beautifully revealing. "Each one who comes brings a contribution, a cupful of meal, or perhaps some rye or graham flour. When the mill management saw how great the interest was they sent us such a supply—meal and butter-substitute and cereals."

"But is it not very hard for you, giving so much of your time and strength?"

Her hand went again in that caressing gesture to the enshrined button at her throat.

"My boy would not have grown tired at his fighting, and why should I? No, I am never weary of it. It's a telling fight. This village is saving pounds and pounds of flour, lard, sugar, and meat. I used to be selfish. My boy was here, handsome and strong and well, and I could make a few dressings, knit a few pairs of socks, use meal and vegetables and corn cereals in my little home, and feel that I was doing my duty. But all that time French boys were being killed by shells and gasses and English boys were being drowned as my boy was drowned. The *Tuscania,* although buried fathoms deep, sent this message to me, 'The tragedy that for four years other mothers have known has this day come home to you. Now—learn your lesson.' That lesson is service in its broadest, truest sense —not our '*bit*' but our *all,* not for ourselves and our nearest and dearest, but for humanity, that justice and right may live.

"My boy has gone from me, but some angel prompted his comrade and friend to send to me this token of his willingness to fight, this pitiful token of the death he died, and, please God, in my poor blundering way I'll do his fighting for him—I'll fight to the finish for my country and his."

Her voice was a mere thread of sound and her face was wonderful to see. She did not look as if caresses would be welcome to her and, although my heart went out in the fullness of sisterhood, I did not offer her such as I said good-bye. A deferential salute, as to a superior officer, seemed more in keeping with a spirit such as hers. But I gave her a sincere handclasp and thanked her earnestly for the wonderful lesson I had learned.

As I went out into the paling sunlight, I seemed to see those rows of lonely graves on the shore of a far away land, and I knew that resting there where thundering billows sounded an eternal requiem was one who had perished not in vain.

THE WRAITH OF AUTUMN
BY
ZOE KINCAID BROCKMAN

———

Awarded the Separk Poetry Cup in 1919

THE WRAITH OF AUTUMN

My thoughts are drunken with you, as the butterflies
   that tremble
And sway in dreamy wonder on the blossom-scented
   air,
I drink the sweetness of you, and I know the hopeless
   yearning
For the sight of you, the sound of you, your touch
   upon my hair.

The tawny wraith of autumn is aslant in all its glory,
Curving to the far horizon with a turquoise at its tip,
The fields are mottled crimson, massed with gleaming,
   uncut rubies,
While the bees from laggard blossoms draughts of
   wind-spiced honey sip.

I loved you in the autumn as white-gowned you stood
   before me,
In your eyes her purple shadows and her sunlight on
   your hair,
And I saw the wonder of her, all her charm and all
   her glory,
In a nuance, softly blended, as a setting for you there.

The wraiths of spring and summer trail their scented
   gowns around me
And breathe of gentle memories that bring you very
   near,
But the wistful wraith of autumn folds you sadly to
   her bosom,
And her leaves chant soft above you as I bless you,
   sleeping there.

THE STILL BORN

BY

ZOE KINCAID BROCKMAN

———

Awarded the Separk Poetry Cup in 1920

(Receiving this award two successive years, Mrs. Brockman became
permanent owner of the Cup.)

THE STILL BORN

You were the flower of my sweetest dream,
The wonder of you thrilled my being through,
Then was it I some ominous shadow cast
O'er your sweet spirit, ere glad breath you drew,
That now you lie within my arms so still
You seem so strange, so very far away,
Yet you were mine, your body stirred and stirred
Against my heart—but that was yesterday.

THE SOUL OF A PILGRIM

BY

SUSIE MORRIS WHITEHEAD

———

Awarded the Joseph Pearson Caldwell Cup in 1920

THE SOUL OF A PILGRIM

IN THE days of Old Plymouth on a cold raw evening in late autumn, two men sat in the Governor's house before a wide, fire-lit hearth, talking and smoking. They were William Bradford, Governor of Plymouth Colony, and his young friend and assistant, Stephen Haywood.

Governor Bradford was a man in the early years of middle life, with a tall, slightly stooped frame and the fine intellectual face of a scholar. In direct contrast to his pale seriousness was the golden-haired, broad-shouldered young giant seated upon a low stool at the Governor's feet, his deep-set, flashing, gray eyes fixed thoughtfully upon the fire. William Bradford, looking at him affectionately, thought of the strange legend among the Indians concerning him. They said that Stephen Haywood had been brought to earth by the great Spirits of Lightning and Thunder, and left during a terrible storm upon the top of a mountain, where, after the tempest had abated, Standish, The-Sword-of-the-White-Man, had found him with the rain drops glistening in his hair and the gray lightning in his eyes and had brought him home to Plymouth Colony to be Great Chief Bradford's right hand. They named him Gray Lightning, and feared him equally with Captain Standish.

In reality, Stephen was the son of a clergyman, Jonathan Haywood, a member of that devoted little band of Pilgrims who, filled with an intense desire for religious freedom, had left home and fireside in England and gone to live in Leyden. Here Jonathan Haywood brought up his son to love God and the idea of freedom above all else. Later he sent Stephen back to England to be educated, and there, as the young man grew older and his strong nature asserted itself, he became thoroughly intolerant of the restrictions and persecutions of his native land and imbued with the ambition to help found a new nation where the worship of God could be carried on in liberty and freedom. Consequently when the Pilgrims set out in the *Mayflower* to found their New World somewhere in the unknown West, they had no two more devoted adherents than Jonathan and Stephen Haywood.

Stephen's life in the New World had been full of hardships and sorrow. During the first terrible winter when more than half the little colony died, Jonathan Haywood was among those who perished, and Stephen with an aching heart laid him tenderly to rest in what was afterwards Old Burying Hill. But Stephen's faith in the enterprise, though sorely tried, did not desert him. All through the struggles, trials, and privations of these soul-trying days, he showed a courage and bravery that made him one of the Colony's leading men. William Bradford became his friend, and their devotion to each other, strengthened in the baptism of mutual sorrow, deepened as the months lengthened into years and a period of comparative prosperity came to them.

It was said, however, that men grew to fear Stephen rather than to love him. His anger was quick and terrible and he seldom failed to discover an injustice and punish the offender. But, throughout the years, William Bradford loved him, for he saw that underneath the young man's hardness of character, there was a heart full of tenderness and a spirit striving to serve God.

This tenderness showed itself in Stephen's face as the two friends talked before the fire, while the clouds hung dark and ominous outside and the winds blew a full gale.

It was to ask a favor that Stephen had called that night. The good ship *Charity* was expected in from England almost any day, and Stephen wanted the Governor to designate him as envoy and lend him the official pinnace in which to meet the *Charity* as she sailed into the harbor.

"Gayly and gladly will I grant your request, my lad," William Bradford replied, "but why so eager to meet the *Charity* that you cannot wait until her passengers come ashore? Is it a new doublet and hose that she's bringing you from London, or something for the Little Gray House?"

"Something for the Little Gray House," Stephen replied, flushing.

Bradford saw the flush and the smile about his mouth, and leaning forward put his arm affectionately around the younger man's shoulders.

"Does this good ship *Charity* then, indeed, mean love for you?"

"Ay, she does," came the answer. "She's bringing my betrothed, Elizabeth Barrister, who is coming to Plymouth to be my wife. I learned to love her when I was at school in England," Stephen went on. "She lived in a little thatch-roofed cottage there, and we used to sit and talk of the home we would build in the New World. She wanted to come with me when I came, but I was afraid—afraid when I looked at her so young and frail and thought of this unknown land. So I persuaded her to wait until I should send for her. That was why, when the *Speedwell* sprung a leak and had to go back to Dartmouth, I begged Dick Wellford to give up the voyage and stay in England to take care of Betty for me until I could send to fetch her."

"So Dick Wellford was the swarthy, dark-eyed fellow I saw you talking with so earnestly that day?" said the Governor, "Me-thought he seemed willing enough to comply with your request."

"Yes, and it's thankful I am that he stayed. No man ever had a better friend than Dick, and it has comforted me ofttimes to think of Betty in his care. She has no kith nor kin except a mother who is old and feeble."

"And to think of your cherishing your secret all this time," mused William Bradford, "building the Little Gray House for your lass o'er the sea, and me chaffing you about it and continually calling your attention to the pretty girls of Plymouth. 'Tis no wonder I could never get you to notice them. What is this Betty of yours like, Stephen? Tell me of her."

"She is very fine and very beautiful," said Stephen simply. "I think she is something like your own wife."

"And a finer compliment you couldn't pay her, you sly fellow," smiled the Governor. "Alice too came from England to me here, just as your betrothed is doing. There is something very wonderful about women like that—weak and dependent—yet with a faith and love in their hearts strong enough to make them leave the comforts and pleasures of their homes and come across the waters to us, who can only offer them the bare necessities of life—and our love. It is something which keeps us on our knees to them the rest of our lives."

William Bradford rose and walked to the fire, presumably to knock the ashes from his pipe, but in reality to hide the look of tenderness which such unusually intimate words brought to his face. He stood looking into the flames a moment, and then continued: "I am glad that you love a fine woman who has courage and faith to match your own, my friend. I hope her coming will bring you every happiness. If you say so, I'll deck the pinnace out in red maple boughs and get Captain Standish and his military men to fire a double salute to the *Charity* when she comes into view."

When Stephen left Bradford, he went home with a step as light as air, and a heart in which all the birds of the forest were singing. He was glad that the Governor had granted his request, and happy to have told his love to his friend, for the bare telling had made it seem ten times more real and more wonderful. There was, of course, much that he had not told, a deal that lay too deep for any ears save Betty's. He had not told his friend that Betty's eyes were as blue as the Mayflowers growing in thickets beside the hedges of England, that her hair was as black as a raven's wing with little tendrils curling about her ears, nor that her mouth smiled and curved up at the corners when she said the sweet funny things which continually fell from her witty tongue.

And the Little Gray House—how could he tell any one what it meant to him! How he had never let any other hands touch it but his own and tried to make it as much as possible like her little home in England; how he had fashioned it carefully and skillfully day by day, with the picture of her ever before him; how he had made her room with its tiny window overlooking the bay, and built the word "Betty" over its door in various colored stones bought from the Indians; how he had planted wild rose bushes around the door, smiling as he thought that even the beauty of their blossoms could not match the tints of Betty's face; how he had read and re-read until they were in shreds the few letters that had come from her, taking them with him up to Old Burying Hill where, seated behind a little thicket of sassafras bushes near his father's grave, he read them again and again.

Stephen's love had grown into his very life. Through the long, hard years it had become a bright and wonderful ideal, the fulfilment of which had taken possession of his mind and soul. And the Little Gray House was its outward and visible sign. Even his religion and his noble ideals, those things which had made him a pilgrim to the New World, became submerged in it, and subservient to it. These things he could not tell his friend—scarce daring to realize them himself.

The days following his visit to the Governor were spent in arranging some of the last details of his house and in anxious watching and waiting. Finally near the end of the third day just as the sun was dying in a riotous mass of red and gold, Stephen, standing in the door of his little house, saw far off across the water a tiny speck which he believed to be the sails of a ship. Eagerly he watched the speck grow larger and larger until the outline of a vessel was clearly distinguishable. Then, catching up his hat and cape, he ran rapidly out of the house.

As he ran, a volley of shot rang out from the Fort on the hill—a military salute to the good ship *Charity*. All along the street women and children came out of their houses. Some of them smiled and called to Stephen as he passed. Reaching the water's edge, he saw the Governor's pinnace with two young men and a boy in it awaiting him. He stepped into the boat quickly and they pushed off through the water.

It seemed to Stephen, as they sped across the bay, that the water between him and the *Charity* was a sea of molten fire and gold. He felt as though they would never cross it. Trying to curb his impatience, he pictured to himself the surprise and delight in

Betty's face when she should see him—the glad sound of her voice as she called to him. How wonderful to have her again after these lonely years of waiting.

The stretch of gleaming water between him and the ship grew smaller. The *Charity* had let go her anchor and was furling her sails. In a moment he would be able to distinguish the passengers. Where would Betty be, he wondered. Was that she—the girl near the middle of the rail, smiling and waving? No, that girl had light hair. Oh, there she was behind that group of men—no, that was an old woman. Eagerly he scanned the faces of the passengers, but the loved face eluded him. Probably she was sick, maybe the long voyage had made her ill.

The little boat drew up beside the ship, and Stephen went aboard. He saw the Captain of the ship, Master Pierce, a friend of former years, and ran to him quickly.

"I am looking for Miss Elizabeth Barrister, Captain Pierce," he cried. "Tell me where she is."

"I have no passenger by that name, Master Haywood," replied the Captain.

"But you have—Elizabeth Barrister—she sailed upon this very ship!"

The Captain shook his head. "I am very sorry but there is no lady by that name aboard. I have a letter here for you though, and a package of letters for His Honor, Governor Bradford. Here they are now."

Stephen looked at the letter. It was Betty's handwriting. He had a feeling of unreality as though he were in a dream. He wanted to push the Captain aside and search the ship. Of course she was there—she had told him she would sail in the *Charity*—he had come to meet her. It was impossible for her not to be there!

His glance fell again to the letter in his hand—Betty's letter. Then it was true—she had not come. Something terribly wrong—she had not come . . . He turned and left the ship.

The crew was letting down the ship's shallop, and many of the passengers were making ready to go ashore. Everywhere was hurry, confusion, and the sound of laughter. Stephen, taking his seat in the pinnace, gave the order to row back to the shore; and the men, after one look at his face, began pulling on their oars without a question. Immediately after landing, he delivered the package of letters at the Governor's house, and then, scarce knowing what he did, opened Betty's letter. The little streaked slip of paper fell out. He read:

"Stephen, oh, my dear, I could not come. I am never coming. I could not take the risks, face the hardships—the dark green waters of the ocean—alone for nights and nights. Oh my dear, I could not come. I am going to marry Dick Wellford, Stephen. By the time you get this I will be his wife. He has been so good to me, so kind, and I love him—not as I loved you, Stephen—no one could be like you. But perhaps it is better so. I am not good enough for you, and not strong enough to help you in that strange new land.

I could never in the old days understand your big ideas about God and freedom. Dick is more like me —some one to laugh with. Oh, Stephen, my dear, can you forgive me? I was not big enough. I had not the courage. My tears fall now as I write. Forgive me, forgive me . . . Betty."

The little paper fluttered out of his hand and fell to the ground. Dazed, he sat looking at it with a numbness growing around his heart. The shock was so great, so over-powering, that realization came only in short, quick flashes. Then followed long periods of apathy, when his mind became a dark void, and he could only repeat, vaguely and unmeaningly, "She did not come," and over and over again, "She will never come."

He did not know how long he remained thus. But, aroused at last by the realization that it was night, that his teeth were chattering and his body shaking, he arose stiff and numb in the cold darkness and made his way to his Little Gray House. As he opened the door, a draft of cold wind struck him in the face like an unseen hand, and he walked to the hearth and raked up the dying embers. He took a taper and lit a candle. As the light flared up it was caught in the colored stones of the word "Betty" over the door and was reflected across the room in a hundred shimmering little lights. A sob rose in Stephen's throat, the candle fell from his hand, and he dropped to the floor in the darkness, his head upon his arms, his whole body shaken with grief. Realization of his loss broke over him at last, and the dark waters of despair closed over his soul.

A picture of the Little Gray House, arose and mocked him—furnished and complete in every detail. And for what? One by one he thought of all the little things he had procured for her happiness—the candles he had dipped, the spinning wheel placed beside the hearth, the chair which he finished but yesterday, the lilac bushes outside the window. She would never see them—they would never feel the touch of her hand! He thought back over the long years of waiting—how futile, how meaningless they seemed now! The cold, the pain and hunger, even the aching loneliness—all this he had stood, and gladly, for he had known he would have Betty in the end. He had loved her so—he wanted her—he needed her . . . How proud he had been at the idea of introducing her to William Bradford and his other friends! He had believed there was no woman in Plymouth one half her equal. Then the realization that she was already married flashed across his consciousness, and stabbed him like the keen edge of a knife. Married to Dick Wellford, his best friend! No wonder Dick had been so willing to return to England to "make the sacrifice for his friend!" No doubt he loved her then, curse him. And the hot blood surged through Stephen's veins as he thought how the man he had loved and trusted had betrayed him. His pain became lost in anger. Red lights spun before his eyes. His hands clenched until the nails bit into his palms. How he would like to get his fingers around the traitor's neck, to choke him, strangle him until he cried out for mercy!

Anger finally burned itself out and a calm, cool plan began slowly to take form in Stephen's mind. He knew at last what he would do. He would return on the *Charity*, the very ship that was to have brought him happiness. Yes, he would return to England when the *Charity* sailed again, and once there he would revenge himself upon the false friend who had ruined his life. Very slowly, very deliberately, would he go about it—no matter if it took years, even a lifetime. But he would destroy Dick Wellford, utterly. He would frustrate every ambition; wreck every plan; surround him with doubt and suspicion; bring him misery, poverty, starvation; and then at last, when he grovelled on the ground, begging for pity, Stephen would kill him, would sink his knife deep into the traitor's heart—that heart so black that it did not deserve to live!

Stephen rose at last, and went to the door of his house. Morning had come; the sun, turning the dark waters of the bay to sparkling blue and silver, shone cheerfully upon the little ship *Charity*, now lying at rest in the harbor. A hollow laugh broke from Stephen's lips as he gazed. A certain grim happiness had come to him with his plan.

During the weeks that followed, Stephen's life seemed to go on as usual. He performed his duties with the same quiet efficiency characteristic of him, giving no sign of the turmoil waging within his heart. He existed through the day in a fever of impatience for nightfall and the lonely quietude of his Little Gray

House. Here, with only the flickering flames for company, he went through his plans for revenge, adding nightly some new detail carefully thought out, and ending always with the moment when he should feel his fingers closing around Dick Wellford's throat and should drive the knife into his villainous heart.

Finally the day for the sailing of the *Charity* arrived. His plans completed, his passage engaged, Stephen awaited with impatience the moment for going aboard. It was morning, and the *Charity* was not due to sail until afternoon—some order of the Governor's—all wrong, Stephen thought. He was anxious to feel the deck beneath his feet, to see the water slipping by, to know that he had actually embarked upon his purpose. He paced the floor of his little house with quick, nervous strides. Suddenly through the tangled maze of his thoughts, came the consciousness that bells were ringing—church bells. Strange, this was not Sunday, and he had heard no order for an official assembly. He went to the door and looked out. Everywhere citizens of Plymouth, arrayed in their best clothes, were going to church. The streets were filled. All at once Stephen remembered. Thanksgiving. It was Thanksgiving Day. That was why the *Charity* was not sailing until afternoon—until after the religious services were over. Governor Bradford had issued a proclamation the day before, Stephen recalled it now, calling upon all the Pilgrims to set aside this day as a day of prayer and thanksgiving to "Almighty God because it had been

His Will to sift the Nations of the Earth, that He might plant His Seed in the Wilderness, and that His Seed had not been choked out, but had lived and thriven."

Almighty God—His Seed in the Wilderness! And to Stephen came an inexplainable longing to enter the church with the others. He ran back and found his hat, but mid-way to the door he paused. Could he go into the church? Could he pray to God? He, a man who was to be—a criminal! But wasn't he already? He had certainly committed murder in his heart. He, Stephen Haywood! He, whose life had been filled with the love of God, he, who had burned to found a great New Nation, he who had so longed for religious freedom that he had been willing to leave all, to suffer all in order to give himself to the service of the Master. Ah! the service of the Master—that was it! And he—this man—was a murderer! A cold sweat broke out upon Stephen's forehead, and his body began to tremble.

The voice of the Pilgrims raised high in glorious thanksgiving, came through the open door—

"God who has saved from wind and storm,"

The music reached Stephen, caught him, enveloped him—and with it, like a flood of light from Heaven, he felt the love and wonder of God flowing over him and encompassing his soul. Tears came to his eyes, and he fell to his knees, crying, "Almighty God, forgive me! Thy Seed in the Wilderness—forgive me. Not my will, but Thine, Oh Lord, be done."

The soul of a Pilgrim had won.

THE CALL OF THE COUNTRY

BY

MRS. ROSCOE L. WALL

———

Awarded the Separk Poetry Cup in 1922

THE CALL OF THE COUNTRY

The call of the country is whispering—whispering,
 Urgent—bewitching, steady and clear,
My tired soul is hearing it—listening—answering,
 Longing to flee from the tasks that are here.

The stretch of the road and the maples are calling,
 The wide-spreading meadows are wishing me there.
The orchard is blooming and soft petals falling—
 The brook sings a melody luring and rare.

The call is so strong that I cannot bear waiting,
 The longing so keen that I suffer its pain.
Ah, come with me, dearest, an end to debating,
 Come! Answer the call of the country again!

THE EXCOMMUNICATION OF
MOTHER HUBBARD

BY

MARY PRESSLY

—

Awarded the Joseph Pearson Caldwell Cup in 1922

THE EXCOMMUNICATION OF MOTHER HUBBARD

LAWSEE-BIMBINY!" Gin'l Bradley took a long breath. "Hit sho am hot!" Gin'l Bradley was six feet four, when he straightened up, and proportioned somewhat like a barrel-stave. Also, he was a little blacker than the dark of the moon. In other words, he was what is known locally as a "Guinea nigger;" and when a tall, thin "Guinea nigger" admits that it is hot, any reliable thermometer will more than corroborate his testimony. It was a very warm day.

Gin'l Bradley stood in the shade of the tulip tree and looked out across the fields that shimmered broilingly in the June sun. A hickory shirt hung widely open at his throat and ragged overalls dangled about his bony legs. Old Beck waited languidly, occasionally jerking a hind foot at a persistent horsefly, or twitching an indolent ear; but she showed no more inclination than her master to begin the afternoon's work.

The old negro plucked at his overalls. "Pears lak I mus' be a-sweatin' glue, way dese-yer britches sticks ter ma laigs," he commented. He looked longingly toward the cabin and the coolness of the well under the big live oak near by.

At that moment the ample form of Aunt Mixie, his wife, blocked the doorway of the cabin, and then waddled cheerfully down the doorstone and across to the well. Gin'l Bradley and his wife were a perfect illustration of the attraction of opposites. Aunt Mixie was a scant five feet from pole to pole, while her equatorial diameter seemed scarcely less. She was garbed in a Mother-Hubbard wrapper, of antique cut, which flapped breezily about her ankles as she walked.

As her husband's eyes followed the billowings of the voluminous garment, they suddenly brightened with inspiration. There was an airy suggestion of coolness about that wrapper, very different from the air-tight stiffness of overalls—even overalls as well ventilated as his. Gin'l Bradley's mouth opened slowly, reflectively. Face and brain labored together in the birth of his idea.

Finally he essayed a tentative question. "Isn' yo' hot, Mixie?" he inquired, solicitously.

His wife flung him a contemptous glance. "I hain't so hot dat I gotter stop workin'," she replied pointedly.

But Gin'l Bradley was impervious to innuendo. "Reckon if I wored a floppy dress lak dat, I'd be feelin' lak work my own-se'f, stidder dese yer overhauls."

Aunt Mixie swallowed the bait. "Well, whyn't yo' put on a dress, den?"

Gin'l Bradley only sighed. "I would, ef I had ary," he yearned, guilefully.

Aunt Mixie looked at him incredulously, then waddled to a pile of soiled clothes under the oak. She sorted out a dingy garment and tossed it toward him.

"Aw-right, dar's a dress. Put dat on, ef you's so pow'ful sot on dresses."

Gin'l Bradley's eyes twinkled, but he strolled with seeming reluctance to pick up the limp frock. Apparently goaded by his wife's jeers, he discarded shirt and overalls, and donned the wrapper. It hung on his gaunt form like a collapsed circus-tent around the center-pole, and it ended, ballet-wise, in the neighborhood of his knees. Aunt Mixie swooned in ecstasy of mirth; but Gin'l Bradley jerked old Beck into action with the rope line, and started majestically toward the field. The mule stopped once or twice to look around at the ungainly scarecrow behind her, but finally decided that it was too hot to be afraid of anything, and plodded on.

Out in the field, the old man chuckled over the success of his scheme. Of course, the cotton stalks scratched his bare shanks occasionally; but the Mother Hubbard flapped about with every step he took, and every flap meant a little cool puff of air. He was rather glad he was not working in the corn-field, where he would have been exposed to the gaze of every passer-by; the long-staple patch was in the rearmost corner of his little farm, far away from every road except a seldom-used trail that led down into the piney woods. No one had passed that way for months, until the week before when Deacon Mose Rippley and his son Odom had gone down to the woods on three successive days, explaining that they were in search of stray hogs. Gin'l Bradley had received the explanation with smiling equanimity, but when they were gone a shrug and a grin had proclaimed his faith in their statement. "Reckon dem's cawn-fed hogs what dey's a-lookin' atter," he had opined; but he decided it was no affair of his, and gave it no further heed.

It was perhaps five o'clock, and Gin'l Bradley was beginning to catch visions of beans and ashcake, when he heard the rattle of buggy-wheels coming up from the woods. The irregularly-steady noise, the "clicketty-clacketty" of ancient spokes in dry weather, sounded strangely familiar; but only when a fly-bitten gray mule wandered up into the clearing did full recognition come to him. It was Parson Phrone Cate's mule; and Parson himself held the reins, with Deacon Rippley seated lurchingly beside him. As Gin'l Bradley neared the fence, they stared at him in open-mouthed amazement; then, as he reached the shade and swung off his hat to fan himself, they suddenly recognized him.

"Wh-why, Brudder Bradley!" Parson Cate's voice lacked something of its usual rotund quality, though it was not un-mellow. "Wh-whut yo' doing?"

"I'se plowin' cotton, Rev'run," answered the parishioner, calmly.

"But—huccome you got on dat—what is dat you got on?"

"Dat's a invention fo' coolness." Gin'l Bradley was fairly sure of his ground, and yet his tone held a hint of embarrassment which was akin to insolence.

THE OLD NORTH STATE

The preacher drew himself up, with unsteady dignity. "Looks mighty quar, nigger; looks mighty
quar," he commented. "Whut you say, Deacon?"

But the deacon was not in a loquacious humor, and
limited his reply to an indefinite "Huh?" and a sleepy
stare. Bereft of official support, the Rev'run jerked
up his mule in disgust, and departed.

Gin'l Bradley scratched his head and gazed after
the decrepit equipage. "Sho is cawn-fed hogs!" he
informed himself. "Yassir! Wonder whar dat still
is at—mus' be down de branch some'ers—'bout whar
dem high bankses is, I reckon. Mistah Joe Deaton he
done say he give twenty-five dollars to anybody what
shows him whar at is ary still—but I ain't gwine tell
nuffin what I doesn't know. Gee, Beck!"

He finished his plowing, and ambled homeward; but
it did not occur to him to tell Aunt Mixie of his
callers.

That was on Friday afternoon; on Saturday morning he wore the wrapper again until about noon, when
there came a heavy shower, which cooled the air, and
also made further plowing impossible. So Gin'l put
on his clean overalls and strolled down to the store.
A group of negroes, mostly pillars of the church to
which he belonged, had gathered under the trees near
the store, and he joined them as a matter of course.
He did not notice that their conversation ebbed as he
approached, but he did notice something peculiar about
their manner. However, some one happened to mention the big "baptizin'" which had taken place the

week before, and in the consequent discussion everything else was forgotten.

When the subject was worn threadbare, Gin'l Bradley remembered that Mixie had told him to bring home some coffee and some thread, so he wandered into the store to make his purchases. As the merchant was wrapping up the meagre bundles, he inquired, jovially, "Well, Uncle Gin'l, what's this trouble you're having?"

"I ain't had no trouble, Mist' Will," declared the old man. "What for you say trouble?"

"Why, when that crowd of niggers was in here a while ago, they were talking about 'churching' you for something—I didn't understand what it was," explained the white man.

Gin'l Bradley looked at him in dismayed surprise. "I ain't heerd nuffin," he affirmed. Then, with sudden reassurance, "Sho, now, Mist' Will, you is just a-sayin' dat." The storekeeper was famed as a tease; but to-day there was no crowd of loafers as audience for his wit.

"No, Uncle, it's the truth," he insisted. Then he came around the counter and laid his hand on the old negro's shoulder. "See here, Gin'l Bradley, I don't know what the racket is, but I'll bet ten dollars you haven't done anything to be turned out of the church for; and if I can do anything to help you, just let me know."

"Thanky, sah, thanky," and the old negro bowed, gratefully. "Nossah, I hain't done nuffin—mebbe dey was jess a-foolin', sah. G'-evenin'."

"Goodby, Gin'l," and the white man went back to his work.

Gin'l Bradley hesitated at the foot of the steps. Should he go over to the crowd with whom he had been chatting, accuse them of double-dealing, and demand an explanation? Or should he wait and let matters take their course? "Reckon I'se gwine home," he decided. "Give a calf enough rope an' he's gwine hang hisse'f, nohow."

All along the homeward path, the old man puzzled his brain over the mystery. Mr. Will had heard something. That was evident; but what could possibly be the matter? He delivered the parcels to Aunt Mixie, then went slowly about his evening turns still studying the problem. His wife noticed his languor, and suggested quinine, but he refused it, unsmiling. He sat on the doorstone after supper, chin in hand, until the mosquitoes drove him indoors and to bed; but even in sleep vague phantoms disturbed him.

In the morning, Aunt Mixie insisted that his heavy eyes demanded attention. "Is you got de rheumatiz?" she inquired, solicitously. "Mout a knowed you'd git somepin, goin' barelegged in de fiel' dataway."

A wave of comprehension rolled over Gin'l Bradley's soul, with the memory of Parson Cate's disapproval of his borrowed garment. "I bet dat's it!" he muttered.

"Want to rub some goose grease on yo' knees?" urged his wife, still intent upon rheumatism.

Gin'l Bradley shook his head mournfully, and struggled stiffly into his "preachin' clo'es," while Aunt Mixie, discouraged in her efforts to render medical aid, proceeded to array herself like the lilies of the field. Presently her husband addressed her. S'pos'n you puts on dat black silk dress what Miss Lucy done give you."

Mixie looked over her shoulder contemptuously. "Huh! Dat dress done wore out. Dat's a mournin' dress, 'sides, an' I hain't mournin'.'"

"Might be, fo' you knows it," hinted Gin'l Bradley; but his spouse had lost patience with his vagaries, and gave no heed.

Out on the path, her temper was tried still further by her husband's erratic gait. One moment he forged ahead, "goin' lak a house afire," she panted from the rear; then he trailed reluctantly along, far behind her. She could not know that his heart was torn with the conflict between dread of the ordeal and the feverish desire to "git it done wid."

When they came into the clearing around the dingy shed dignified by the name of "Ebenezer Church," she left him, and waddled away to join a group of women who were putting themselves into a Sabbatical frame of mind by pulling weeds from the graves. Just then, however, Parson Cate came to the door and rang a little hand-bell energetically, and the negroes scattered about the clearing began to stroll toward the building. Gin'l Bradley fell in with a group of his usual colleagues, but they ignored him coldly. So he trailed in lonely misery to his accustomed seat near the pulpit.

Parson Cate began the service with dignity, and announced the hymn, "I Want to be Like Jesus in my Heart." Aunt Mixie, from her seat over by the window, "histed the tune" without waiting for Melinda Cate to play the prelude on the organ, and the older members of the congregation joined in lustily, not heeding the disgusted glances of the more sophisticated younger element. The singing dragged on interminably, one long-drawn-out and much-repeated verse after another, while tardy comers straggled noisily and cheerfully to their seats. Finally it ended, and Parson Cate prayed, long and loud, with special and pointed reference to "sinners in our midstes" and "wolves in our bosoms." Gin'l Bradley felt that many eyes were upon him, and squirmed inwardly. Other hymns followed, interspersed with prayers by various pillars of the church; but Gin'l Bradley was not called upon to lead.

At length the time for the sermon arrived, and Parson Cate, after much turning of leaves, announced his text, "The woman shall not wear that which pertaineth to the man, neither shall a man put on a woman's garment." The word "pertaineth" gave him considerable trouble, but finally he got it pronounced, after a fashion of his own, and began his sermon. He discussed in full the question of women's dress, ancient and modern, and took occasion to express his opinion of the styles worn by white women, particularly those given to the foolishness of horseback-riding. From this he drifted into a description of the absurd costumes worn by "town niggers." So, at last, he approached the real point toward which the preamble had been tending, and which Gin'l Bradley was expecting. Smug grief sat upon his unctuous countenance and wailed in his voice as he stated that in their midst was one who had sinned most reprehensibly in the matter of dress. Aunt Mixie's eyes were fixed upon the stretch of limb protuding from a Paris-short skirt where Melinda Cate lolled on the organ-stool; but the parson's thoughts were not upon those of his own household. He launched into a fiery denunciation of the awful sight which had recently met his eyes, "right out in a hones' cotton-patch whut God A-mighty made!" ("Didn'," contradicted Gin'l Bradley, impiously, under his breath. "I made dat cotton-patch my own se'f, chopped de trees an' clared de bresh.") The audience listened breathlessly; those who knew the object of this harangue thrilled with the pride of superior knowledge, and the ignorant waited fearfully for the dénouement. Presently it came; and the Rev-run' expressed his belief that Gin'l Bradley, having worn "dat which—er—which p-p-puttneth to a woman," had disobeyed the Holy Scriptures and was therefore unfit for a place among the true saints of Ebenezer Church.

A sigh, half of approval, half of dismay, swept the audience; but from Aunt Mixie, at first rendered speechless by such mention of her lord and master, came a reproachful, "Oh, Lawdy!"

The preacher glanced at Deacon Rippley, and in response to the signal the deacon stepped forward, and moved that the congregation expel the offender. Somebody seconded the motion (Ebenezer Church prided itself on conducting all business in a lawful and legal manner); there were two or three impassioned speeches, by special adherents of the ruling element, and the deed was done.

Gin'l Bradley was stupefied by the cut-and-dried suddenness of the whole proceeding; but when the parson, leaning over the pulpit to pronounce sentence, pointed a fat forefinger at him and commanded, "Git dee hence, Satan!" he awoke. Slowly he unfolded himself to his full height, glaring meanwhile at the parson until that gentleman shrank a little, even behind the shelter of the pulpit. After a prolonged survey, Gin'l Bradley opened his mouth. "I hain't no Satan," he explained, "but I'll git. An' I'll git you too, you blame-fool ole nigger whut call yo'self a preacher!"

There was evidently more—much more—on his tongue, demanding utterance, but he checked it, grimly, and strode with heavy-footed dignity toward the door. A wailing avalanche stumbled after him; for Aunt Mixie, heart-broken to the point of hysterics, was yet loyal. If her "cote-house" husband was to be "run outen de church" for wearing her Mother-Hubbard, she would run along with him.

Gin'l Bradley tramped homeward in stern silence, while behind him Aunt Mixie filled the woods with her screams and sobs, with an occasional pause to express in no gentle terms her opinion of the Revrun' Cate and his leading deacon. To her surprise, the outcast did not stop at the cabin, but walked steadily on, down the path that led to "de fur fiel'" and the woods beyond. To her shouts of remonstrance, he paid no heed at first, until she became so vehement that he turned and spoke with patriarchal authority, "Ole woman, shet yo' mouf!" Thereupon Aunt Mixie sank upon the doorstone, a convulsed mountain of despair.

Gin'l Bradley tramped on, past his cotton-patch, and into the woods. When he came to the branch, he followed the little stream down toward the low bluffs which marked its junction with Big B'ar Creek. Stepping carefully, to leave no telltale prints, he searched diligently up and down, until he found that for which he sought, and registered its location exactly in his mind. Then he hurried back to the cabin, where Aunt Mixie still mourned dolefully upon the step; and her he addressed in tones of righteous indignation. "Ole woman, whaffur you hollerin' dataway? Git up. I wants ma dinner."

"Who keers for dinner, when you done got turned outen de church?" wailed his wife.

"I keers. An' gettin' turned outen old Phrone Cate's church ain't nuffin. Jess you wait. Dat ole fool nigger he jealous 'case you kin sing better'n dat yaller Melindy ob his; but he'll hab more'n Melindy to study 'bout by-m-by."

"What you mean, Gin'l?" There was the dawn of hope in Aunt Mixie's tearful eyes.

"Nebber you min' now. Jess git atter dat dinner. An' keep yo' mouf shet. Whut you don't tell ain't gwinter hurt you." With which piece of philosophy, Gin'l Bradley betook himself to the shade of the live oak. So it came about that when certain of his former co-religionists passed by, en route home from the thrilling service which had followed his expulsion, he was sitting serenely tilted back against the well-house, smoking his old pipe and apparently indifferent to the whisperings and gigglings with which they had recognized him.

On Monday morning, he donned the Mother Hubbard again, in spite of his wife's pleadings; but this time he turned Beck's nose to the cornfield which paralleled the main road, and here he gee-hawed lustily until noon. He kept his eyes and ears open, however, and ambled home at dinner time well satisfied with the result of his observations. To Aunt Mixie's eager questions, he responded only with grunts, interspersed between mouthfuls of beans. When he had eaten, he changed from the wrapper to his overalls, and started out toward the store, vouchsafing no satisfaction to his wife's curiosity.

To his joy, there were no loafers in the store, and he approached the proprietor cautiously. "Howdy, Mist' Will?"

"Howdy, Gin'l? What can I do for you?"

"Nuffin, thanky, Mist' Will. I'se jess projeckin' 'round a little." A pause. Then, "Say, Mist' Will, dey done turn me outen de church yis'day, lak you say."

"Did they, sure enough?" The white man's tone was sympathetic. "Well, now, that's a shame."

"Oh, hit's all dat ole Phrony Cate's doin's. He's been a-aimin' to git me an' my old woman out fer a long time; Mixie kin sing better'n Melindy."

"Uh-huh!" The white man's grunt expressed his comprehension. "But what did they say was the reason?"

Gin'l's description of the circumstances leading up to his expulsion sent Mr. Will into convulsions of laughter, but it was not unkindly laughter. When the negro had concluded his tale, he asked, "Mist' Will—you reckon dey's ary way I kin git de law on Phrone for doin' me dataway?"

His friend considered the problem carefully. "No, Gin'l, I don't know of any law that would apply. You don't by any chance own the building, do you?"

"Nossir. Mist' Will, you knows dat church-house is on de corner of Mr. Frank Brown's woods. Even de burying-yard is his'n."

"Well, if you should buy that land from Mr. Brown, it would be your church, wouldn't it?"

"Yassir."

"How much rent does Phrone pay him?"

"I dunno, sah. Reckon he jess lets him hab it."

"Well, if I owned it, I'd charge two dollars a month for it, and rent it to the first nigger who asked for it."

"How long could anybody git it for twenty-five dollars?"

"For a year, and a dollar over. I'd throw in two or three months extra to anybody who paid in advance. Are you planning to rent it?"

"Nossir—nossir! I was jess a-askin'. But, Mist' Will—you reckon dey's anything I could do about dat lawin' business?"

"I don't know a thing," declared the white man. "But Sheriff Deaton went up the road this morning, and he ought to be coming back pretty soon. You might ask him."

"Yassir; yassir. I jess mosey 'roun hyar a while an' see do he come."

Gin'l Bradley's scheme was working exactly as he had planned. He rambled about the store, studying the familiar shelves and showcases, with their assortment of goods that varied from plaid ginghams to patent medicines, from raisins to pitchforks, from coffins to watches. Then he went out and took a nap under a tree across the road.

Presently he shuffled back to the store. "Mist' Will, I done hear a autybile way up de road; effen dat's Mist' Sheriff Deaton, you reckon you'd ask him to stop?"

"Sure, I'll stop him for you," said the white man, good-naturedly. He strolled out to the porch in time to hail the sturdy driver of a rattling car. "Hey, Joe! Got time to stop a minute?"

"Yes. What do you want?"

"Nothing. But here's an old negro wants to ask something."

The sheriff looked appraisingly at Gin'l Bradley, stepping forward with evident pleasure in this publicity. "Well, old man, what is it?"

"Mist' Deaton—I heard as how you say you gib twenty-five dollars to ary nigger what shows you whar at is a still?"

"Yes. What of it?" The sheriff's tone was crisp.

The storekeeper looked quizzically at the old negro; evidently this was not the conversation he had expected.

Gin'l Bradley went on, "Effen dat's right, I kin show you a still right now."

There ensued a sharp cross-questioning by the white man, and stubborn reiteration by the negro. Then there was some cautiously-worded telephoning and the gathering of two or three more white men. Some hours later, the sheriff resumed his journey toward town, accompanied very reluctantly by Parson Cate and Deacon Rippley. Also, a peculiar combination of twisted copper and other metals, with sundry bottles and jugs, went along as evidence; and back in the woods was the wreck of a paying industry.

Gin'l Bradley had kept well out of prominence. But he was standing beside the store when the party drove up, and as the sheriff went in, the old man ambled in after him and stood waiting, unostentatiously. Mr. Deaton noticed him upon leaving, and said, "Well, old man, come down to my office to-morrow and your money will be ready for you."

Gin'l Bradley's face fell; the sheriff's office was in town, ten long miles away. But Mr. Will was still to be his good angel, for he said, "I'm going to town to-morrow, Gin'l; be up here soon, and you can ride with me."

"Thanky, sah, thanky. I'll be proud, sah." Gin'l Bradley stepped off briskly down the path. Aunt Mixie had apparently been watching, for she joined him as he entered the woods, and bombarded him with eager questions. He informed her curtly that the parson and the deacon were en route to jail and to a probable term on the roads, whereupon her anxiety was changed to a shout of rejoicing. But her husband, with the dignity becoming an arm of the law, commanded silence and supper, and Aunt Mixie obeyed, muttering, yet with new respect in her manner.

In the morning, Gin'l Bradley rode happily to town, received his check, and, with Mr. Will's assistance, got it safely cashed. He deposited the bills carefully about his person; no monkeying with banks for him. On the way home, Mr. Will asked suddenly, "Gin'l, do you know anybody that wants to rent Ebenezer Church?"

"I—I d'no, sah. Whaffer you ax me?" Gin'l Bradley was not quite sure what was expected of him.

"What do you suppose I went to town for?"

"I d'no, sah." Gin'l Bradley's manner implied, respectfully, that he felt it was none of his business.

"Well, I went to have a deed recorded."

"Yassir." Gin'l Bradley seemed to think that was a very proper thing for a white man to do.

"It's a deed to some land I bought from Mr. Frank Brown."

A moment of acquiescent silence, then, "Lawsee, Mist' Will!" Comprehension, gratitude, wild ambition, surged forth with the interjection. "Mist' Will —kin I rent dat church?"

"What do you want of a church?" The white man seemed genuinely surprised by the proposition.

"I—I jess wants it. Reckon I kin hab a church as good as Phrone Cate."

"Sure you can, Gin'l. And, since it's you, I'll rent it to you a year for five dollars, if you'll pay in advance."

The old man began to fumble with sundry knots and buttons, but his friend checked him. "Hold on— wait till we get to the store. Your money will blow away here."

So presently a bill changed hands, and the old negro went home bearing his fortune of twenty dollars and a receipt duly written out by Mr. Will, stating that one General Bradley was the sole lessor of Ebenezer Church for a year from date, with absolute authority over all services therein.

The week that followed was one of much activity, lingual and otherwise, in colored circles. On Sunday morning, Gin'l Bradley and Aunt Mixie, garbed in their best, walked briskly to church. The congregation, scattered about the dooryard as usual, looked at them askance as they stepped haughtily into the building; but a few, who had been among the lesser lights of Parson Cate's flock, greeted them smilingly. Aunt Mixie walked to her old seat; but her husband, having rung the assembly-bell, took his place behind the pulpit. The congregation came in, a little dubious; strange rumors had been in circulation.

Gin'l Bradley arose, pleasantly dignified. "Ladies an' gemmuns, breddern an' sistern," he began. "Probably you-all has heerd as how dey's been some changes in dis-yer church. De evil-minded an' de hypocrites has fell, an' de righteous has been 'xalted. I is now de—de—"

"Lessor," prompted Aunt Mixie, in a fierce whisper.

"De lessor ob disyer preachin'-house, an' ary nigger what ain' gwine do lak I say an' 'have hisse'f, kin git out." He paused for signs of rebellion. "Right now!" he added, emphatically. There was no movement in the audience. "Very well, let us sing, 'Swing-A-Low, Sweet Chariot.'"

Melinda Cate, sitting as usual in the amen corner, arose, a trifle uncertainly, and started to the organ, but Gin'l Bradley stopped her. "Let dat orgin alone, woman. You keep yo' mouf shet, an' let dem sing as kin sing. We hain't gwinter hab no town fiddle-dee-dee. Mixie, h'ist de tune."

Aunt Mixie, duly impressed by her husband's authority, raised her voice in a rich quaver, and her friends joined in, while Melinda Cate furnished a reedy obligato of sobs. Her mourning continued audibly through the long prayer that followed the singing; and immediately after his "Amen!" Gin'l Bradley suggested that she leave the building until she could control herself; so she stepped out, still weeping.

Gin'l Bradley opened the Bible, slowly, impressively. One page was as legible to him as another; but he fumbled the leaves until he thought he had given the proper effect, and then traced out a passage with a slow fore-finger. Mr. Will had coached him carefully on his text, and he pronounced it aloud, still pointing to the printed words before him. "Man looketh on de outward appearance, but de Lawd looketh on de heart."

"Glory! Hallerujer!" shouted Aunt Mixie. "Bress de Lawd!"

A CRY

BY

CAROLINE A. TROWBRIDGE

——

Entered in the 1922 Contest

A CRY

Out of my dark despair
  I cry aloud;
"Is my beloved there,
  With thee, O God?"

"Mother," a Voice replies,
  "Thy love is here,
Beyond the darkening skies,
  Beyond all fear."

"Into the vale of death
  Shadowed and dim,
Lord, till his parting breath,
  I went with him."

"Mother," the Voice replies,
  "Blessed thou art!
Since closed his weary eyes,
  Upon thy heart."

"No farther could I go,
  My God," I moan;
"Where the deep waves o'erflow,
  He went alone."

"Mother," the Voice replies,
  "Oh, not alone!
From death to Paradise,
  I lead my own."

"My God, would I had gone—
  Holding his hand—
Till o'er him rose the dawn
  Of that far land!"

"Mother," the Voice replies,
  "I held his hand,
Till waked his happy eyes,
  In mine own land."

TRANQUILITY

BY
EDNA BAKER SCRIMGER

Entered in the 1922 Contest

TRANQUILITY

All still things thrill us with their loveliness:

The glorious burst of sunrise without sound,
The dew-laved freshness of the tender ground;
And still, so still, between the earth and sky
The clouds on phantom footsteps going by;

The willow tree in spring with swaying branches,
The sky at sunset ere its splendor blanches;
Unopened buds and butterflies at rest
A soft dove calmly brooding on her nest;

Bring to the heart a loud tumultuous joy
That all the stillness round cannot destroy;
An untranslated voice of exultation
A singing silence filled with jubilation!

Yes, still things thrill us with their loveliness.

THE SEEKER

BY

ZOE KINCAID BROCKMAN

———

Entered in the 1922 Contest

THE SEEKER

THIS IS the place, Etoile. We will stop. Are you sure that you are quite willing?" The man, young and bronzed and broad of shoulder, stopped the roadster before a small weather-stained house on a rugged mountain road, and turned to the girl at his side.

Her eyes shone mistily through a grey motor veil, a rough gray coat swathed her figure. That she was small and slight was evident in spite of the smart shapelessness of her motor togs. Her foot in its smooth kid boots was arched and slender, the grey gloved hands wonderfully small.

The man carefully disentangled the loose ends of her soft veil from contact with the fixtures of the car, and peered through its cloudy greyness into her dark, shining eyes.

"Quite willing, Etoile?" he questioned again—eagerly, gently.

"Surely, Jack. Else why should I be here?" Her voice was throaty, with a peculiar, foreign tone.

"I was thinking of him, the other man, Etoile. I want to be sure that you're regretting nothing—I've been so insistent, darling! I want to *know* that it's I you want, not he."

"It has always been you, Jack, ever since you came. He—I've never cared for him. It was Tante, and the others. It was all arranged, you know. They—

he's older and—settled. And then, of course—rich. I don't know—it seems—"

"Never mind, Etoile. I've heard it all before. Older and richer and more settled, and prominent! Is that all, or are there other qualifications? Oh, yes—family! The alliance in prehistoric ages of some branch of his family with some branch of your own." The man's voice was edged with irony, but it became suddenly tender as he leaned toward her.

"But—you don't love him, Etoile?"

A slow flush mounted beneath the grey veil. "Love him?" she echoed gravely. "How can you ask? I love *you*."

He bent and kissed the veiled face swiftly. "Then, forget them, darling-aunts, guardian and all. You've never disobeyed them before, little wee convent dove. Why, you little Frenchie! Our girls don't ask whom they may marry, nor do they sit tamely by and see it settled for them. The aunts will forgive you. I'll see that they do—or choke them if they don't."

The girl did not smile. She merely sat quite still until the car door was opened and Jack Kirkland's strong arms were outstretched for her. He caught her to him, quite off her small feet, held her for an instant breathless and close, and then released her quickly. They walked silently, hand in hand like children, up the narrow, shell-bordered path to the little weather-grey house.

The old minister who performed the simple marriage service was quite blind. His spinster sister, old and very deaf, placed his hands in blessing upon the two young heads when the simple words had been said, as she had done many times before. Etoile noticed that the names as they were written in the ponderous marriage register could scarcely be recognized as their own. The spelling on the marriage certificate, painfully written out by the woman's gnarled old hand, was the same. She felt the stiff newness of the paper as she tucked the certificate way beneath the scented laces at her breast. The ring pressed hard and cold against her finger. Jack was talking to the old man, laughing. She asked for a drink of water, there was a rattling of tin pail and dipper, the water was very cold. Presently Jack was helping her into her coat, was calling her "Mrs. Jack Kirkland," they were driving away.

To the day of her death Etoile would remember the feel of the blind old man's soft flabby hand in her own, the toneless rasp of the deaf old woman's voice.

The spot Jack Kirkland had selected for their honeymoon camp was as beautiful as it was secluded. A slender grass-grown valley, it ran like a flat green velvet ribbon between massed purple-topped hills. Their small striped tent made a bright spotch of color against the green hills, drooping trees stood guard about them, bubbling water allured them with its witching music.

Etoile, pale and rather silent, exclaimed over the delicate beauty of the wild ferns and flowers. Holders in which to place them were produced from the camp kit, filled with water and fastened to the taut walls of the tent.

While Jack, a splendid young god in his outing flannels, built their first camp fire, Etoile slipped away to the tent and exchanged her grey motor gown for a soft trailing negligee of marvellous Chinese blue, wondrously becoming. When she returned to him, her bright, soft hair in two lovely, loosened braids about her bare shoulders, exquisitely embroidered mules on her slender feet, Jack Kirkland caught his breath at the new, intimate loveliness of her. Together they sat on a flattened rock at the foot of a royal singing pine, and dreamed young dreams in the light of their first home fire.

"Happy, Etoile?" he whispered, her body fragrant and soft against his heart, her drooping, grey-blue eyes sweet beneath their sooty lashes.

"Happy—ah, Jack!" The breathless words gave to him his most intimate glimpse into her heart. That she loved him he knew. That she was about to be pressed, passively enough, into an unwelcome marriage with an old family friend he also knew. That she would have married Cordiss Haynes, stout, reserved, and middle-aged, and lived out uneventful, peaceful days he was sure of, had not he, Jack Kirkland, prevented it by carrying her away and marrying her himself. Body and soul and spirit he loved Etoile Carstairs. Body and soul and spirit Etoile loved him in return. But she would have gone to the altar with Cordiss Haynes, the love for Jack Kirkland burning in her heart, and would have felt that she was fulfilling only her simple duty toward those who had arranged the eminently suitable marriage for her. The aunts and her guardian were anxious for Etoile's future. They did not like, nor did they approve of Jack Kirkland. Etoile's mother, another oval-faced, brown-haired, demure person, had married, some twenty years before, the stalwart Englishman, Frederick Carstairs, because her family had said that she must. She had not loved him, nor had she been happy in the dreamed-of way during the few short years that she was his wife, but she had been true to the principle of obedience to her elders, and deference to their wishes was her second nature. And now her daughter, Etoile Carstairs, who could not remember a mother, and to whom the slightest words of the aunts had always been law, must unquestionly entrust the happiness of her future to them. All of this Jack Kirkland knew, —the instinct of silent submission born within her, the influence that had been brought to bear upon her. And with it, surmounting all else, was the new, sweet knowledge that Etoile was his own—the youth and sweetness of her, the artless gravity of her quaint, foreign ways. He stooped and kissed, reverently and very tenderly, the sweet crimson mouth.

For one perfect week they lived and loved and dreamed in a golden world of their own, away from any human sound save that of their own voices, in a veritable Eden that had not yet been transgressed. They spent long hours before their nightly camp fires,

STORIES AND POEMS FROM

the present a haven of blissful contentment, the future
stretching like a rainbow-spangled mist before them.

At the end of the week they returned in a measure
to material things. They talked of going back to the
world again, wearing the magic cloak of their new
happiness, of facing the angry coterie of Etoile's relatives, of renting a flat. Etoile was very silent. She
lay passive against her husband's breast, her bright
thick braids thrown about his shoulders in a fanciful
way of her own.

"Do you want to go back, infant?" Jack questioned,
pressing one by one her soft rose-tipped fingers to his
lips. She drew a strange long breath, half gasp, half
sob.

"No, Jack," she answered, her eyes tightly closed,
her lashes a line of curved jet against creamy cheeks.
"I don't wish to go back—ever. Only—of course we
must."

"Necessarily, sometime." He laughed cheerily,
pinched her pale cheek, and set about to replenish the
fire.

That night while Jack was sleeping Etoile crept
softly out of the tent. Its orange stripes were bright
in the moonlight, the world seemed very still. She
crouched before the sinking embers, thinking. She
had thought much in the last few days, even with
Jack's dear arms about her. She, Etoile, had done a
grievous wrong. She had come away with Jack, had
married Jack, while her aunts thought her visiting a
convent friend, and when, in two short weeks, she was

[138]

to have married Cordiss Haynes, the choice of her guardian and of the aunts she loved so dearly. She had been taught explicit obedience and she had willfully, grievously disobeyed. She must live for years and years, perhaps to be an old woman. Could she live with the aunt's grieved faces forever reminding her of her disloyalty to them, beneath her guardian's hurt, reproachful eyes? Perhaps Jack would take her away—but he could not take her out of the world. Her family would have smiled upon her had she married Cordiss Haynes. She would not have been a sinner, then. Her fingers slipped nervously over her polished rosary. Cordiss Haynes was a good man, a rich man. It meant much to marry a rich man—beautiful houses, soft linen. Tante had taught her this. The aunts wished it, her guardian wished it, it was all arranged. A girl had no right to show such flagrant disrespect to those older than she, to whom she owed so much. She had been taught well, and she had erred grievously. She bowed her head, the beads slipping quickly between her fingers. Tears moistened her eyelids and all else slipped out of the world save the dark blot which lay between her well loved family and herself.

The certificate of marriage pressed harshly against her soft breast. She remembered Jack's face as he had taken her hand into his own in the little painted sitting-room of the weather-grey mountain parsonage. She remembered that she had been married by a Protestant minister and with the Protestant service. The old minister's blind, sunken eyes, the queerly spelled words in the marriage register, the vapid faces of the witnesses rose with horrible distinctness before her mental vision. She shivered before the white ashes of what had been their glowing camp fire and suddenly felt tired and ill.

It was near day break. Jack was yet asleep, his blue pajamas open at his breast, his throat showing white beneath his tanned face. His head against the white pillow was moulded like a god's, his face like the faces on old Greek coins. Etoile bent softly above him and laid her cheek for a moment against his own before lowering the grey motor veil from the hat she wore. From the pocket of her coat she took two papers and slipped them gently beneath his folded hands. With a single glance about the silent tent she went noiselessly out and down the leafy path to where the little roadster was housed among the trees.

The sun was pouring its molten glory through the side of the white and orange tent when Jack Kirkland awoke. He turned and smiled across at the twin cot opposite him before he saw that it was empty. Etoile was gathering flowers for her vases, he mused. Raising himself slowly on one elbow, he heard the crisp rattle of paper. Still smiling he reached for Etoile's letter. The certificate of marriage was folded with it.

"Dearest Jack," she wrote. "You said if I did not marry you you would go to Africa. Will you not go, now? Indeed you must, for I myself must go away.

It was wrong that I came away with you—they were always kind. They do not expect me to disappoint them, and indeed I cannot. The verb 'to love' I have conjugated all the night through! 'We have loved,' oh, so much. Will not that do, Jack? Do not be sad, dear. Forget all else save that we have loved, and that, long, long ago."

ETOILE.

"You will destroy the paper, will you not? Then it is all in the past. If we do not remember, none will."

Jack Kirkland's face stiffened as the words sank into his understanding. He read the faintly written lines twice through, crumpled the letter fiercely, and then smoothed it gently out again. Poor little Etoile. Poor little frightened child. Only the American-bred child of a French mother and an English father could have so sadly entangled the affairs of her heart with her sense of justice, loyalty and obedience. Her feeling of allegiance to her relatives was pathetic. She had been torn between her love for him and what she considered her filial duty to them. She had tasted of heaven, had sipped of the god's own wine, and she had gone back to her piteous, arduous duty. For the first time he read the marriage certificate quite through, noted the mis-spelled, illegible words, and understood Etoile even more clearly.

Because Jack Kirkland was a dreamer of dreams he could not leave the shell of his Great Dream to the elements. With lips and jaw set like an Indian's, he broke camp. On the spot where the tent had stood he dug an oblong opening, six feet long and four feet deep, and very carefully lowered into its depths the folded tent with its flaunting white and orange stripes. Upon it he laid the linen, the Navajo blanket which Etoile had whimsically stretched across the door of their dream-house, the gay pillows, the little pewter knives and forks. Then he tore the marriage certificate into infinitesimal shreds and sifted them in a pale shower over the wreck of his Dream. He filled the opening with painstaking care and mounded it. From beneath the pine tree he dragged the tablet of rock from which, on their first evening together, they had watched the sparks of their camp fire melt into the thick purple night. With infinite patience he carved the initials "J. K." and "E. C." and when he had finished threw his spent blade into the long grasses and rolled the stone to its place at the head of the mound.

"For it is our grave, Etoile, yours and mine," he mused, a whimsical, uneven smile twisting his lips. Arms folded, he stood quite still, looking down at his work. "All of good or of happiness that was, or is, or could ever be for either of us lies there. Goodbye, Etoile, poor little child of duty whom love could not hold."

The shadows gathered the valley in their weird, long arms, the peering stars bent down for a diadem, and still he stood, dark brows drawn down above anguished eyes, the twisted, curious smile on his lips.

The announcement of the marriage of Etoile Violet Carstairs and Sidney Cordiss Haynes came on the day that Jack Kirkland sailed for Africa. Among his fellow-passengers was a missionary's wife—tall, thin, and badly dressed. The grave, bronzed young man with the shoulders of a god and a face like the faces on old Greek coins, moved her to question the steward concerning him.

"Going to hunt tigers, is he?" she said, in response to the steward's sparse information. "Well, he looks as if it would take more than tigers to frighten him." And then, with a woman's afterthought, she added, "Is he married?"

"Married," scoffed the steward. "That man ain't got no time for wimmen." And because he was fat and asthmatic the steward wheezed as he laughed over the missionary woman's fancy.

Later, when the *Mongolia* was wrecked, the missionary's wife, as one of the survivors, never tired of telling how Jack Kirkland, "gay as a boy at a baseball game," helped the women with their little ones to the boats, and then the men, waving them on when they stopped to urge him to take his place among them. And finally how, before she closed her eyes to the sights and sounds around her, she saw the big wave surge murderously toward Jack Kirkland, who faced it arms folded and his eyes on the western horizon. "The bravest man I ever saw die, and I've spent twenty years on the mission field," she would conclude, wiping her eyes hastily with a long, bony hand.

Mrs. Cordiss Haynes is a popular woman and very beautiful, in a strange, magnetic sort of way. Her dark eyes burn with a peculiar, lasting brilliancy that strangers remark upon. Her hands, very white and slim, with the blue veins showing clearly through, have a curious way of hovering nervously over objects within their reach—flowers or jewels when she is wearing them, the tea things, the silken draperies, and of drumming noiselessly upon the table or music stand before her.

When a celebrated Polish artist wished to glorify his canvas with her brilliant, piquant, restless face, a curious friend asked what he could call the portrait. He replied promptly, "The Seeker."

"The Seeker? Of what?" pursued the curious one.

"Of what?" smiled the artist as he strolled away. "Ah—that is the unanswered question."

THE MERCIFUL GOVERNOR

BY

NELL BATTLE LEWIS

Entered in the 1922 Contest

THE MERCIFUL GOVERNOR*

The man who used his recent high estate
Often to break the prisoner's galling chain,
To lead the hopeless exile home again,
To show the wanderer a path made straight;
For whom it was delight to speak the word
That brought glad light where darkness cast its fears;
Whose joy it was to dry Disgrace's tears,
And utter what the bowed heart, leaping heard;
Now has himself been loosed, the binding clay
Hampers no longer; Death, who guards the Door,
Hearing the mandate of the Governor,
Opens it now to a new flood of day;
Generous of wide unfettered liberty,
Cries to the captive spirit, "You are Free!"

* This sonnet was written in memory of the late Governor Thomas Walter Bickett, who was noted for his kindness of heart in pardoning prisoners.

[147]

6

MY DAY

BY

MRS. ROSCOE L. WALL

———

Entered in the 1922 Contest

MY DAY

I thank Thee, God, that I may have my day—
  The sweet green wonder-mist of childhood's morn,
When make-believe o'er nature holds full sway,
  And all the wild delights of games are born.

I thank Thee for the joyous throbbing noon,
  When romance casts its charm within my heart.
And o'er the hills comes riding—all too soon—
  The Prince—of whom I've dreamed so oft, apart.

And for the afternoon of motherhood
  When life's sweet joy and pain have stood the test,
Love's light glows brighter, better understood,
  In these sweet hours, I think my day is best.

And when the evening of my life is come,
  While looking back on all the trodden way,
I'll watch in sweet content the setting sun
  And thank Thee, God, that I have had my day.

THE HOUSE OF LIFE

BY

MARY PRESSLY

Awarded the Joseph Pearson Caldwell Cup in 1923

THE HOUSE OF LIFE

HENLEY GAITHER closed the trunk and turned the key. It had been at least ten years since he had packed his own clothes. "Osano might have waited long enough for that," he muttered, bitterly. But the little Jap had taken his departure hours before, with many protestations of regret, and yet with an intangible lack of his old deference. The other servants had already gone.

"Rats out of a sinking ship!" snarled Gaither. He stood back, panting, and glowered at the trunk. Then he jerked on his coat, snatched his hat, and slammed out of the apartment. The elevator boy bowed politely, as usual, but there was appraisal in his glance.

"Just a buzzard, like the rest of them," grumbled Gaither, as he tramped aimlessly down the street. "Anybody can peck at a fellow when he is down." He wondered if the papers had anything new about him today. He seemed to be a regular celebrity. Well, it wasn't every man on Wall Street whose partner had run off with a stenographer and left the firm to absolute ruin. And she was such a quiet, modest-looking girl, too. Women were all alike, anyway—scratchy cats, or vamps, or fools of some sort!

Suddenly he realized that he was mumbling his thoughts aloud and gesticulating with a clenched fist. People were looking at him curiously. He would certainly have to take something for those confounded nerves.

A familiar doorway attracted his attention. His club dues were paid, anyway. There was still one place where he had a right to go and rest a while.

He found himself breathless as he climbed the steps. He did not like the way the old doorman stared at him; but then, everybody was staring these days. "I believe I'll go out and turn handsprings in the street, and let them stare in earnest," he told his favorite big chair in a corner of the smoking-room.

Two or three men in the opposite corner stopped their conversation to look at him.

He had never noticed before how close the air was in that room. It surely needed better ventilation. The house committee ought to attend to it. He decided to go back to the street. The handspring idea had returned to him.

"I might as well be hung for a sheep as a lamb," he informed the startled doorman. "I'll do it. But I'll have to wait a while. My head feels queer. I think there is gravy in it now. It's scorched gravy, too. Mutton gravy, I reckon."

He giggled, and the man recoiled, horror-stricken. Gaither dashed past him and out of the door. The Park would be a good place for his gymnastic stunt. But between him and the Park was a broad street, ripped by a million automobiles, and every one of them was determined to run him down. He started, dodged, backed, tried again; and then there was a traffic police-man waving a frantic signal that he could not under-stand, and then a speeding little flivver, and then— nothing!

That was in November. It was early in March when he stood white and tremulous in the hospital office and received his discharge. The doctors had been very kind, very patient; they had explained about irregular hours, and nerve-strain, and careless diet, and lack of recuperative power. Henley Gaither did not listen, for the verdict they had pronounced was reeling through his mind. "Six months; maybe longer, with favorable conditions." Six months! Six months —and then—?

Presently he was out on the street. It was cold and snowy, but there was a hint of spring in the wind that shouted up from the south. Always the south wind had touched a responsive chord in him; even in frantic devotion to business he had felt it like a call from home. Far to the southward his home lay, a substantial old stone house among the Carolina hills. He had not seen it for half-a-score of years, not since he went to his mother's funeral; since then the house had stood closed and lonely. It had been twenty years since he had lived there; he was just one-and-twenty when he came to the city to seek his fortune.

Well, he had found it, and lost it again. And in the finding of it, and more especially in the losing of it, he had lost a greater fortune; he had lost most of his faith in men, and all of his faith in women; and now he had lost his health,—and the final loss only six months away. He had nothing left.

Then he remembered that during all these years a shame-faced bit of sentiment had kept up his taxes on

Gaither House. Most of the plantation had been sold, but he still owned a few acres, and a house that was middle-aged, as houses go, when red-coated soldiers marched by it on their way to Yorktown.

Suddenly into his consciousness leaped the old legend of Gaither House, that quaint superstition which he had almost forgotten. For nearly two centuries men and women of his blood had lived there, but none had died there; not one of his race had closed his eyes for final sleep in the house where first he had opened them. The Gaithers died, of course, like other mortals, but they had always died away from home, by accident or sudden illness; and so had grown up the eerie fancy that Death could never enter those oaken doors.

A fantastic idea came to him. He was a Gaither. If a Gaither could not die in Gaither House—

He laughed at himself for a fool. He was not superstitious. An old legend based on coincidence meant nothing to him. What nonsense it was!

But an hour later he was at the bank, inquiring about his slender balance. During the rest of the day he roused the ghost of his old-time efficiency and drove it sternly to the tasks he appointed, until night found him, spent and weary, in a Carolina-bound Pullman.

Twenty-four hours later he held himself upright, by sheer will-power, on the rear seat of a dilapidated surrey that floundered wildly along a dark and rutted road. Around him rattled and rustled a conglomerate heap of bundles, hastily purchased at the village store.

He felt utterly exhausted. Dying would not require much effort. What was the use of postponing the operation? In six months, anyway, if those doctors knew their business, his coffin would be bumping along that road toward the cemetery at old Gaitherwood Church.

"Poor coffin," he pitied, grimly.

The driver stopped, and got out to fumble with what appeared to be a gate between tall posts. He struggled for some time, and finally, with an oath, flung the mass crashing to one side. He investigated a little, and then came back to the carriage.

"Look here," he began in an aggrieved tone. "I can't drive no horse up through all them bushes and weeds. This place has been shut up for ten years."

"I know," replied his passenger, with feeble dignity. "I ordered it to be kept locked. But is there no way to get to the house?"

The memory of sunken eyes and trembling limbs, seen in the murky light of the station, moved the driver to pity. "Wait 'til I light your lantern," he offered, "and I'll walk up with you and see you in all right."

He tied his horse to the fence, shouldered an armful of packages, and flickered the lantern boldly through a wilderness of neglected growth. When they reached the house Gaither was breathing painfully. The driver led the way cautiously over the uncertain footing of the porch, and held the light while his passenger unlocked the door. The lock was rusty, but at last it yielded, and a vigorous push from the driver's fist released the stubborn hinges. There was revealed a wide hall, with large rooms on either side, and massive pieces of old furniture covered with dust and cobwebs.

The driver stared in simple curiosity. To Henley Gaither, the sight was a vision of the past. The rooms were just as his mother had left them ten years ago. A queer faintness seized him, and he staggered to a chair.

His companion spoke brusquely. "Look here, sir, this place ain't fitten for a sick man. Better ride back to town and stay at the hotel to-night. You can come out again to-morrow if you feel better."

"No." Henley Gaither was determined. "If you have time to help me get things in order—of course I'll pay extra—"

"Sure, I'll be glad to help you. And that's all right about pay. I ain't got no more trains to meet to-night." He plunged back to the surrey for Gaither's bags and another armful of bundles. He propped open such windows as were movable. He tested the chimney with a bit of blazing paper, and, finding the draught satisfactory, built a roaring fire. He went off, lantern in hand, on a tour of back rooms, and then climbed the echoing stairs, coming back to report, "The beds all smell right musty. You got some blankets, ain't you? Better sleep down here by the fire—that is, if you won't go back to town. I won't charge you nothing to ride back. This is a awful lonesome place, and some folks say it's ha'nted; ain't many men but me would come here at all."

"Nonsense!" The voice would have been curtly superior but for its tremor of weakness. "But if you know anybody who passes here on the way to town, I wish you'd ask him to stop in to-morrow—I may need to send for something more."

"Sure. Let's see—I'll call up Jim Herndon. He lives just next above your place, about a quarter of a mile. He's the accommodatin'est man around here."

"I remember him. Tell him I'll pay him, of course."

"Not Jim Herndon, you won't," laughed the other, easily. "Jim might be better off if he'd charge folks for what he does, but he'd lack a heap of being as happy as he is now. He'll be tickled to death to bring out stuff for you. Are you sure you'll be all right now?"

"Yes, thank you; good night."

"Good night, sir." The man crashed away through the underbrush, and Henley Gaither was alone in the home of his fathers.

He expected to lie awake most of the night, fighting the nervous headache which usually tortured him with half-delirious terrors. He felt sore and bruised; the hours of travel had jarred every weakened muscle almost beyond endurance. Those last fifty miles on the jerky little local train, and then the jolting ride out from town, had left him utterly worn. But the headache did not come on with its usual violence. Instead, through the open window came a crisp little breeze, with the breath of the mountains on its lips; somewhere out in the trees a bird murmured sleepily; far away the faint barking of a dog.

Henley Gaither sat upright, muffled in his blankets. The fire had died to black ashes, but the room was bright; it was flooded with sunshine that blazed in through the open door. There was no doubt about it; it was morning. He looked at his watch. Nearly eight o'clock! He had slept for ten hours.

He was stiff and sore and utterably miserable. The floor was unmercifully hard. He struggled out of his blankets and into his clothes. The wind which swept through the house was cold, and yet there was strength in it, like a torrent of iced wine. The man had left a supply of light-wood beside the hearth, and he kindled a little fire and shivered in its warmth.

The thought of food was nauseating to him; but memory of his purpose in coming to Gaither House forced him to search among the bundles. Twenty years of city life had not destroyed entirely his boyish lore of camp cookery; so presently a coffee pot simmered on a bed of coals, and the scent of broiling bacon arose from a long-handled frying-pan. He ate the bacon from the pan, and drank coffee from a collapsible cup in his bag. Then he lay down again.

Every bone in his body was a separate and distinct pain. He did not feel able to get up, and yet contact with his hard couch was torture to his tender flesh.

By and by he dozed again, and awoke to slow consciousness. He arose and staggered to the door. It stood widely open to the east, where the sun was climbing steadily up the sky. Far below shimmered the windings of the river, and beyond were wooded hills. He gazed over the familiar scene until weariness drove him to a chair. After a time he stumbled slowly to the rear door through which the west wind was sweeping in. He looked out to barns and stables, crumbling into ruin, to a patch of weeds and briers where once had been a garden, and to a ragged old orchard. Further still were rolling hills and clumps of woodland interspersed with bare fields; and far away, heaped along the horizon, were the tumbled masses of the Blue Ridge mountains.

"Hello?"

It was a girl's voice, gaily inquiring. He turned quickly, and caught at the door-case to steady himself. She stood framed in the sunlight, so he could not see her face, but only the buoyant lines of her figure.

"Good-morning! Are you Mr. Gaither?"

Henley Gaither, walking painfully forward, admitted his identity.

"I'm Ginnie Herndon. Somebody phoned out from town that you wanted to see us about something, but the wires roared so I couldn't understand him."

"Oh, no, Miss Herndon—I'm sorry." When a man's whole will-power is devoted to the effort to keep from sprawling to the floor, it is hard to speak naturally. "The man who brought me out last night promised to ask Mr. Jim Herndon to attend to some errands for me."

"Oh, was that it?" The girl laughed. "Well, there's no harm done. I thought maybe you needed something right away; we heard you were sick. You do look rather white. I believe you ought to be in bed."

"I've been there." Henley Gaither felt quite helpless. He wished she would go away. He didn't want
to be bothered with girls, and especially with a girl
who was so annoyingly alive as this one seemed to be.
Irritation made him dizzy, and he began to sway. Before he knew what was happening, the girl had caught
his arm and was leading him to a chair.

"You *are* sick," she insisted, anxiously. "Wait a
minute and I'll get you some water." She darted
toward the rear of the house and almost instantly she
was back.

"Look here!" she reproached him. "Are you actually
trying to stay in a house that's been deserted for ten
years without having it fixed up at all?"

"What's the matter? It's my house, isn't it?" Fret-
fulness had mastered courtesy.

"Of course; but why didn't you have it cleaned?
Don't you know that stagnant water out of an old well
like that is pure poison?"

"Is it?" A certain amused mockery had come back
into Henley Gaither's tone. "Will it ease your mind
if I tell you that I have a bottle of mineral water with
me?"

"Oh!" The girl's manner had hardened instantly
in quick response to his. "I beg your pardon. If
there is nothing I can do for you, I'll go home. My
father is going to town this evening, and I'll ask him
to stop and see about your errands."

"Thank you. Of course I shall pay him for his
trouble."

Her head went up. "We are not wealthy, Mr. Gaither," she replied, haughtily. "But we are not poor enough to be paid for a little kindness to a neighbor. Father will be glad to accommodate you, sir. Good-morning."

She vanished quickly among the trees.

She was angry. Well, he didn't care. Maybe now she would let him alone. He was utterly weary of women, anyway. How thankful he was that he had never married! He'd be dead soon enough, without any assistance from some nagging female.

It wasn't the fault of the women that he had not married. There had been plenty of Delilahs willing to shear him for the golden fleece—no, that was mixed metaphor, or something, but at least it was the truth; they were all alike. There had been one that he had thought was sincere, but—well, he was too tired to feel the old hurt now.

He leaned back in the chair and watched a squirrel scamper up and down one of the big oaks beyond the door. Its mate followed, and the two of them ran boldly up the steps and peered in at him. When he moved, they darted away, scolding.

Those steps looked really unsafe, in spite of thick planking and heavy beams. If only he felt a little better, he would like to mend them.

He didn't feel better. He wanted to rest. He thought of the hard floor, which his blankets could not soften. There were beds upstairs, but that long flight of steps was a lion too fierce to attack. But, of course!

His mother's old room was downstairs, convenient to both parlor and kitchen. He walked stiffly back to investigate. The driver had missed that door, some way, in last night's scheme of ventilation, and the room was close and foul. He opened windows, laboriously, and the healthful fresh wind swept in. The bed was musty, but it was soft; he dropped across it, and relaxed.

He was still lying there, some hours later, when a masculine "Hello?" roused him. Lazy indifference kept him from answering the hail; but it was repeated, and then footsteps came into the hall, inquiringly. They approached his room, and a tall figure came in.

"Well, Henley Gaither! What are you doing laid up in the bed that way?" Jim Herndon's big voice was natural as ever. "Sure seems good to have this place opened up again. Been pretty sick?"

"Yes." Gaither could not bring himself to say more. His guest's brusque cheer grated on his nerves.

"That's tough. But say, you oughtn't stay here alone. This room still smells bad, too. Why can't you come over to my house and stay till you can get things cleaned and fixed up?"

"No, thank you. I prefer to stay here." Everybody was in league to get him away from his refuge, but he wouldn't go. Gaither House seemed his only security.

Big Jim Herndon was booming on about the need of well-cleaning, and bed-sunning, and kindred activities. That girl must have given a thorough report.

Henley Gaither interrupted with a curt remark about his needs in the way of groceries, and Herndon took the hint. That was one good thing about the Herndons; father and daughter were alike sensitive to hints.

It was late afternoon when Herndon returned, and tramped up the brushy lane with his bundles. Gaither still lay across the bed.

Herndon was worried. "Look here, ain't you had no dinner?" he demanded.

"I haven't felt hungry."

"Well, man, you can't lie here and starve. Are you going to try to cook for yourself?"

"Yes." Evidently he would have to give another hint.

But his guest was not looking for hints. "Now, Mr. Gaither, that ain't right. A well man ain't no good at cooking for himself, let alone a sick man. Say, why not get old Aunt Liza Gaither to come over and cook and do around for you? She's old, but she sure can work. She beats these young niggers all to pieces."

"Aunt Liza Gaither? Liza? She used to be my nurse." Slow recollection pictured fat black arms that were the cradle of his childhood.

"Sure, that's the one. I knew she used to work for you-all. I think old Jim, her husband, was one of the Gaither niggers before the war. I'll try to see her to-night or in the morning. Hope you sleep well. Good-by."

He was gone before Gaither could protest. On second thought, he was not sure that he wanted to protest. Oh, well, he could afford to pay her for a week or two; wages would be less here than in New York.

The afternoon sun crept further and further across the room. The deadly faintness of the morning had returned, and with it another feeling, a strange gnawing that he could not understand. It had been years since he had felt really hungry.

He became conscious of noises. There were subdued rustlings, and light stealthy footsteps. It didn't matter; thieves were welcome to anything they might find. Later on, perhaps, he would go out and investigate.

After a while some one came swiftly through the hall, and Ginnie Herndon appeared at his open door. "Mr. Gaither, do you feel able to come out to supper now? I brought over a few things from home, for father thought you were too tired to fix anything yourself."

The girl certainly was persistent. He might try, just to get rid of her. He stumbled out to the dining-room. She had laid a clean cloth over one end of the table, and was setting dishes out of a basket.

He wasn't hungry; but when she put a bowl of soup before him, the odor was not unpleasant. He sipped, and sipped again; and, before he knew it, the bottom of the bowl stared up at him. The girl had gone out of the room; but now she was back again, and slipped away the empty bowl and put something in its place. There were biscuit, two of them, hot and flaky; there was an egg, cooked just right; there was half of a luscious peach, with clear syrup; there was a glass of fresh milk.

He found himself wondering, fancifully, if the Herndon girl had ever worked in a restaurant; she seemed to have learned the trained waiter's knack of effacing herself absolutely and yet appearing whenever she was needed.

He ate slowly, and looked out at the low sunset light that trailed goldenly among the trees. There was nothing to hurry him, no meeting of boards or commissions, no engagement to go somewhere in formal clothes and be bored. It was restfully quiet. Sometimes a mocking-bird trilled in ecstasy. He heard the girl's footsteps occasionally, and wondered what she was doing.

He nibbled, and sipped, and looked out of the window, and listened to the silence; it was nearly an hour after he sat down when he realized that the dishes were practically empty. He has eaten a meal and enjoyed it, for the first time in months.

The room was darkening into twilight when she came in, carrying a lamp.

"Do you want to sit here a while, or would you rather lie down now?" She asked it as impersonally as might a professional nurse. He discovered that he was still tired, and chose to rest.

"Then I'll put the light in your room. I've been straightening up there a bit, and I think it will be more comfortable. Good-night."

The lamp had flickered across the hallway almost before he found his feet. He caught a glimpse of her as she flashed out the rear door, and later he heard a gentle clinking of dishes, but she did not come near him again.

He had been too long used to trained servants to understand just what she had done to his room; but it did not seem so dusty, and there was a clean odor, not nauseating like hospital disinfectants, but healthful. A little fire blazed happily in the chimney. Something had happened to the bed, too; it was opened invitingly, and there were fresh sheets, and blankets which certainly were not the musty covers among which he had lain all the afternoon.

Yet he did not fall asleep as he had done the night before. He lacked the opiate of physical exhaustion. His old headache began to come back. The bed was soft, and very comfortable by contrast with his couch on the floor; but various joints and muscles began to complain, and found bumps which nagged them. He slept a little toward morning, and awoke haggard and unrefreshed. He felt too tired to get up, and yet he was too tired to lie still. He moved restlessly in search of comfort.

When heavy footsteps lumbered at the back door, and a throaty contralto called, "Mist' Henley, kin I come in?" he was annoyed. Evidently Herndon had carried out his threat; but there was no using trying to avoid his old nurse now. She came waddling in, smiling cheerfully, and he endured a season of greetings and exclamations and questions. When at last she left the room, he was exhausted. He heard her outside in low-toned conversation with some one, and presently she brought in a tray and insisted that he eat his breakfast in bed. He was not hungry, but he forced himself to nibble a little before she took the tray away.

He lay in bed all morning, irritated by sounds of prodigious activities in the region of the kitchen. There was a continuous squeaking, too, which seemed to come from the old well. He decided the Herndons must be up to something.

Days passed, and he lay in stupid languor. His old servant had reconstructed his bed, replacing the mouldy mattress with a tick full of fragrant straw. Every morning she urged him into an easy chair, while she shook up the tick into fresh comfort. She swept and dusted too, sketchily. At intervals she brought in a tray, and coaxed him to eat a little. For the rest of the time she left him alone, to lie and listen to queer commotions throughout the house, or to doze in the intervals of silence.

Early in April, there came a morning when the bright crispness of the world seemed a tonic to his soul. After Liza had departed ponderously with his breakfast tray, he struggled out for a tour of exploration. The doors stood open, and the wind was whooping gaily through the hall. The house seemed changed. Careful inspection showed that everything had been thoroughly cleaned; there was not a speck of dust anywhere.

From the kitchen came a pleasant little sound of irregular tapping, that reminded him in some way of childish Christmas anticipations, and the beating of sweet plummy batter. He shuffled cautiously across the porch, and peeped in at the door. By the table, her hand jerking rhythmically above a yellow bowl, stood that Herndon girl. She flushed at sight of him, but greeted him calmly.

"Good morning, Mr. Gaither." Her tone was pleasantly remote.

"Good morning. Where's Liza?" He could not keep the irritation out of his voice.

"Oh, she just found that one of her hens was coming off, and I told her to go on and look after the biddies and I'd finish the custard."

Her yellow dress made a bright spot of color in the dim old kitchen, and some men would have found her flushed face attractive to look upon; but Henley Gaither only grunted, and strolled back to his room and the restful haven of his bed.

That afternoon he explored again. The girl did not appear. The custard came in on his supper tray, but he did not eat it.

Further investigation discovered more work done while he lay in bed. The house was all in order. Undergrowth had been cleared to allow passage between the house and the gate. Aunt Liza was using water from the well, and told him her nephew had cleaned it thoroughly.

Sharp questioning brought out the fact that "Miss Ginnie" had overseen the cleaning, and "Mist' Jim" had ordered the outdoor work. Apparently the Herndons had taken him in hand.

No doubt they looked upon him as a heaven-sent source of profit. It is easy to be interested in a sick millionaire.

"Aunt Liza!" He spoke abruptly. "I want to see Mr. Herndon. Send for him to come over here right away."

"Yessah, jess soon's I see somebody goin' along dat way," promised the old woman, cheerfully. "But I don't reckon he kin come 'fore night. He's pow'ful busy plowin' right now."

Gaither turned away, and went back to another rest on his bed. There was no use in arguing with her, and her easy familiarity annoyed the man who had grown used to instant, anxious obedience to his orders.

The night was mellow, and after supper he dragged a light chair to a sheltered corner of the porch and watched the birth of a golden moon behind the hills across the river. The scent of "green things growing softly" drifted to his nostrils. He lay back, indolently, while the lazy moon climbed a ladder of fleecy white clouds.

It was a pretty good old world, after all; too bad he had only six months more to enjoy it. Six months? He had been here a month! He had only five months left!

A figure moved among the shadows on the driveway; some one was coming toward the house. When Gaither recognized Jim Herndon, his face hardened.

After a friendly greeting, the visitor suggested, "Did you want to see me?"

"Yes." Henley Gaither hesitated a little. It was going to be harder than he had thought. "I understand you have been looking after things around here, had the well cleaned and the like; and your daughter had been supervising Liza."

"Oh, that wasn't nothing." Jim Herndon seemed embarrassed. "I hope you didn't think we was taking too much on ourselves, but it had to be done and you wasn't able to do it."

"That was thoughtful." A little cynical undertone edged the words. "But evidently you have not heard that I am practically a pauper. I shall try to pay for what has already been done, but it would be unwise for you to incur any further expense."

"Mr. Gaither!" There was a hurt quaver in Jim Herndon's voice. "Sure, we heard all about your trouble. It was in the papers. Ginnie and I felt mighty sorry to think an old neighbor had had such hard luck; and if we'd a knowed you was coming we'd had the place fixed up when you got here. We didn't go to no expense that we could help. Of course, I had to pay Bill for cleaning the well, but it wasn't much, and you can settle any time you feel like it. And Liza won't charge much for the cleaning. She wants to move into that little house in your yard, and she'll do your cooking for the rent, if you give her most of her time to herself. She makes a right smart, washing for people in town. So you needn't worry about expense."

"But—your own time, and your daughter's?"

"Forget it," urged the man. "It didn't take us ten minutes to show them niggers what to do; and all the work on your drive was one wet day when I couldn't plow nohow. And Ginnie wouldn't be happy if she had to stay at home all the time. It's fun for her to run around and look after the neighbors' affairs. She's always been crazy to see inside this house, anyway."

Henley Gaither did not speak. He had not been accustomed to people who did favors out of pure kindness of heart; there was always, somewhere, the sly hand waiting for the tip. Yet he could remember nights when his mother had stayed away from home to care for some sick neighbor who could not afford a nurse; his mind pictured black Sam, gathering up a load of wood which was to be dumped in old Widow Henderson's yard, "wid Mis' Gaither's compulments"; he himself had made careful selection of balls and marbles, which were his donation, along with his mother's gifts of quilts and a table, to a family whose home had been burned. Yes, it was the custom of the country; not a very business-like custom, to be sure, but strangely heart-warming.

Jim Herndon was rambling on about the weather, evidently with a view to covering any embarrassment his host might feel; but presently he unlimbered himself preparatory to starting homeward.

"Thank you for coming over, when you are so busy." Gaither's voice lacked its normal curtness. "I am very much obliged to you—and your daughter."

"No occasion, no occasion," answered the other, heartily. "Ginnie and I are all that's left of the Herndons around here, and you are the only Gaither, and it's a pity if we can't help each other out."

"Well, if ever I can do anything for you, let me know," the invalid found himself saying; and then his lip curled in the darkness, at such an offer from a dying man.

But Jim Herndon took it as a matter of course. "Thank you, I sure will."

Every day Gaither sat out on the porch, and looked at the birds and the squirrels, and watched the soft spring growth of trees and flowers. But the disorder everywhere in the grounds annoyed him.

Beside the porch there had been a bed of buttercups, and two or three of them were still trying to push feeble heads through a maze of weeds. It was too bad for them to have to die; he knew how they felt. The porch was low, and by sitting at the sunny edge he could reach the buttercup bed with the cane which he had found somewhere. There was a particularly ugly nettle that seemed trying to usurp the whole bed. One day his irritation could endure it no longer, and he began to poke it with the cane. He kept punching and prying, until the roots gave way, and he tossed the thing to one side, triumphantly. The effort left him gasping; but he found the scent of raw earth, ripped up in the struggle, singularly refreshing.

There were some vines that smothered the porch, and they fretted him until he hobbled to the kitchen for one of Liza's big knives, and boldly hacked away the trailing ends.

Every day he saw something that worried him until he corrected it. Then he began to notice things inside the house that needed attention. He found a hammer and some nails, and steadied the shaky newel-post. He congratulated himself that he had made rather a neat job of it; the nail-heads were not obtrusive and there were no hammer-scars on the polished wood.

When Aunt Liza asked him about shelves, he hunted out the old lumber in one of the sheds and tinkered and sawed and hammered for a week.

When the shelves were finished, the rose-bushes began to bother him. So he dug, and pruned, and carried buckets of rich earth from the deserted stables. It was tiresome work; he had to rest between trips, and sometimes he lay down for half-a-day.

Then the weather grew warmer, and Ginnie Herndon, coming over to ask the privilege of gathering a few early apples from his orchard, rebuked him for exposing himself to the sun. He had never ceased to resent the girl's attention, and her intrusive desire to help him always irritated him; but the many favors he had accepted from the Herndons forced him into apparent courtesy.

"Help yourself, of course," he invited; "I didn't suppose any of those trees were bearing now."

"Oh, yes, some of the old trees have fruit, and there are a few young volunteers. The apples aren't as fine as if they were cultivated, of course, but they are good for pies, and ours won't be large enough for a week yet."

[177]

She flashed lightly through the house, and he heard her calling gay nonsense to Liza as she passed the cabin.

When he strolled to the cool dining-room for his supper, he found a saucer beside his plate with a triangle of green-apple pie. If that girl had brought it, he wouldn't eat it. He was about to ask, and then he reflected that he had neither seen nor heard her since morning. Aunt Liza had access to the orchard, of course; probably Liza had made it. It looked good. It tasted good, too; he ate the whole piece.

The summer dragged away, slowly, and yet not unhappily. Before and after the heat of the day Henley Gaither pruned, and hammered, and tied up, until by September the immediate vicinity of the house had assumed a fairly respectable appearance. There was much to be done, of course, which he could not attempt; a new roof, for one thing, and the clearing of two or three acres of brush that stifled the lawn, the repairing of barns, the rejuvenation of the orchard.

He had little company. A few men of his own age had dropped in to see him, and he had been glad to meet them; but when they had finished their reminiscences of boyhood days, they had little in common, and the visits were not repeated. Some of his mother's old friends drove out, and he received them courteously, but politely refused their invitations; they did not try the rough road again, but they sent out occasional peace-offerings of home-made cake or preserves. He was glad to be let alone.

The elasticity of his finances surprised him. He had bought no new clothes, to be sure, and his weekly accounts from the grocery seemed infinitesimal. At city living rates, the little he had saved from the wreck would have lasted him barely his allotted six months; he was amazed to find that here it would be sufficient for another year, at least.

Oh, well, he would not need it another year; his time must be almost up. He began to calculate; then he went to the kitchen to consult the lurid patent-medicine calendar hanging over Liza's work-table.

It was the tenth of September; it had been the tenth of March when the doctors pronounced his doom. In six months he was to have been dead; but he wasn't dead; he wasn't a bit dead. Methodically he began to take inventory of himself. He was weak, he was still frightfully weak; he had to spend a good part of every day in rest, but he was not sick. Headaches rarely troubled him now. He slept well almost every night. He ate regularly, and enjoyed his food. In fact, he enjoyed living; that was it, he enjoyed living. In the old rushing days of business, he had not lived; he had only worked, and felt delirious excitement when he succeeded. To enjoy the mere fact of being alive had never occurred to him then. It was queer.

Well, his time was up. He supposed he would die soon. Of course, the doctors had said it might be a little longer. Anyhow, he might as well fix the loose shutter while he could.

The days were still hot, but there was a flame of black-gum here and there in the woods, and the wind from the mountains brought a tingle of expectancy. Something in Henley Gaither's blood responded to its crisp tonic and he found his rest periods growing shorter, there was a hint of energy in his movements.

September passed, and October was almost gone. Blue haze veiled the mountains, and lay soft upon the hills beyond the river where the trees clung jealously to gorgeous rags of crimson and gold. The music of hounds hot-foot on fresh trails came up through the morning mists and the distance-mellowed crack of guns echoed across the browning fields.

Henley Gaither rode to town in Jim Herndon's rattling car, among sacks of sweet potatoes and crates of squawking hens. His purchases were soon made; and in the interval of waiting, he strolled into the dingy little hotel. Two or three traveling men were lounging about, when the far-away shriek of a locomotive made them snatch up their bags and scurry off toward the depot. One of them flung down a paper as he left his chair and Gaither picked it up, aimlessly. It was a New York daily, and instinctively he turned to the market pages.

"Hm!" Things must be lively on Wall Street; steel and wheat playing hide-and-seek, and everything else sympathetic. If he were in the pit now—

He threw down the paper and went out to look for Herndon. On the homeward road he was grumpily monosyllabic; and Herndon, after a questioning glance, turned his entire attention to his driving.

Left at his own gate, Henley Gaither threshed out quick decision. He was certainly well enough to handle business. His head was as clear as a bell. He could take the train on Saturday night and be in New York in time to have a good sleep before business hours on Monday. He would finish that Sanderson bunch this time. First, though, he would go see the doctor, and find out how much longer he had. It seemed rather absurd to plan for making more money, when he would not live to enjoy it; but he could give it to the Herndons—and at least he would have the satisfaction of paying the Sandersons back.

As to things here—well, Aunt Liza could stay on in her cabin; and he would engage Jim Herndon to see that the place was kept up so he might come back for a vacation some time. Oh, no, he had forgotten; he would soon have no need of vacations. He would go over and talk to the Herndons to-night, anyway; and to-morrow night he would start back to New York.

He was tired when he reached the Herndon cottage, and accepted gladly the big chair which Ginnie pulled forward.

"I know you are tired; this is the first time you've walked over here," she sympathized. "But it is just wonderful the way you've gained since you came home. I think this is the best climate anywhere."

"Are you an authority on climates?" He tried to speak playfully, but there was almost a sneer in the question.

"I suppose that does sound silly," the girl agreed with his thought. "No, I've lived here all my life, except when I was at school in Virginia for three years; but I've read and studied about all sorts of places, and it seems to me there is some drawback to every one of them. I think if people here would all live as they should, they might be perfectly well."

"As they should?" queried Gaither.

"Oh, live reasonably, you know, and eat wholesome food, and work enough for good exercise, and keep clean, and enjoy life generally."

"Do you enjoy life?"

"Of course I do. There is so much that is worth while. Just to get out these mornings and look across to the mountains, and listen to the dogs down in the bottoms—it makes me so happy I want to fly."

Gaither laughed indulgently. "But don't you want to travel, and see the cities, and have beautiful clothes and jewels?"

The girl's eyes grew a bit wistful. "Yes," she admitted, honestly; "I'd love to try them for a while. But I don't believe such things could make me happy all my life. They are all attractive, but they wouldn't fill the corners of your soul like the simple little every-day things—flowers that grow in your own garden, you know, or a motherless lamb that you raise by hand. And all I've read and heard about cities makes me think I'd be lonesome; but here I know everybody for miles around, and if any of the neighbors are sick I can go over and help—"

She stopped in sudden confusion, but Gaither finished her sentence, "As you did for me. And that reminds me, I want to thank you for all your kindness—you and your father. Is he at home?"

"No, I'm sorry; one of the negroes in the Hollow has a sick mule, and father took some liniment down for them to try. But he ought to be back before very long."

"I was going to ask him about looking after things for me while I am away," began Gaither, but he was checked by the girl's startled look.

"Are you going away? Not for good?"

"I hope so."

"Oh, you know what I mean—to stay?"

"Yes, I think so. I have loafed long enough. I thought perhaps Mr. Herndon would be willing to keep up the place for me."

"Of course he will; but we had hoped you were going to settle here and work up the plantation yourself."

"That's kind, but I wouldn't be here long anyway."

Her wide eyes questioned him, and a boyish longing for sympathy broke down his reserve. "You see, I had a pretty bad collapse before I came here." She nodded. "And the doctors told me I could never be well again. In fact, they gave me just six months to live."

"Six months!" Anxious horror edged her voice, and then she brightened. "Oh, but they were mistaken—it's more than six months since you came?"

"They said it might be a little longer, with favorable conditions."

"But you're so much better. Why, you are well now! You aren't going to die! Oh, I don't believe it—I can't believe it!" She was leaning forward, her bosom heaving.

Henley Gaither studied her, critically. She was really pretty. He was touched by her interest; and it was surely sincere, not the dainty flattery he had met so often. "Oh, I might as well be dead," he drew her on. "I am a poor man, without any friends to care what becomes of me.

'Rattle his bones
Over the stones,
He's only a pauper, whom nobody owns!'"

"Don't!" The word was sharp. "You have no right to talk that way. You are not a pauper. And you musn't speak as if you had no friends. Why, I—"

"Would you care?" he asked with new gentleness.

A slow color grew up in her face, but her eyes met his, steadily. "Indeed I would," she told him. "You went away when I was just a child, but you have always been a sort of fairy prince to me, and I was so glad when you came home, and I have looked forward to having you for a real neighbor; but now you are going away."

Her voice almost broke; and Gaither checked himself sternly. These simple people had given him the first disinterested kindness he had received in years; and, while he didn't like the girl, it would be despicable to punish her intrusion by flirting with her. Just then he heard Jim Herndon's cheery whistle in the yard, and spoke with relief, "Here comes your father now."

Herndon was genuinely sorry to hear of his plan. "Why, we're just beginning to get acquainted with you, and we sure will miss you. Ain't you coming back some time soon?"

"If I do, it will be to Gaitherwood Church."

Jim Herndon stared, but Ginnie broke in with report of the doctor's prophecy. Her father repeated her challenge of the verdict. "Oh, man, it can't be. You don't look sick. I don't believe it. Maybe coming here has cured you. You know that old story about Gaither House, and how the Gaithers can't die there? I reckon the place has gone the story one better this time, and cured you into the bargain."

Henley Gaither's habit of reticence yielded to the friendly interest. "You may think it foolish, but really that old legend was what brought me down here, I believe; I knew it was nonsense, but I seemed to feel that the old place was really a house of life."

"And yet you are leaving it?" The girl's voice was almost a wail.

"Yes, I think I'll try to get back at the fellows that picked my pockets before; and maybe I'll go around and see the doctors again."

"Oh, do; and you'll let us know what they say, won't you?" She spoke eagerly.

"Well, yes, if they allow me another term, I'll write you and ask you to wish me luck in business."

"But why do you want to go into business?"

"Oh, I need to make some money."

"You can make all you need right here." She spoke positively. "If you would work up that strawberry patch this fall, you could make something off it in the spring, and the garden would bring in a good deal through the winter, if you plant onions and salad greens. And you can easily raise enough sweet potatoes to pay your grocery bill; there's always sale for them at the canning factory. And you could get a reliable cropper, and the rent would cover your other expenses."

She meant it; and he had heard a woman whine because her pearls cost only fifty thousand dollars, and wish she had a husband who wasn't stingy.

"Now, don't worry, Mr. Gaither," suggested Herndon. "You want to go, and it ain't no use arguing with you. But we sure do hate to see you leave."

Gaither pondered the situation as he strolled homeward. There had been many girls who were interested in his personal affairs, while his bank account made their interest worth while. There was a little salve to his vanity in the possibility that a girl might be interested in him for his own sake. Common sense shattered the fancy by suggesting that the Herndons would always be interested in everything that needed help; Jim Herndon had been interested enough in a sick mule to take a long walk after a hard day's work.

Ginnie was really a likable girl. Of course, he did not care for her, but he did not dislike her as he had done six months before; her excessive vitality did not annoy him so much, since there was less of contrast with his own languor.

He went to New York; and the crash and rattle of the city greeted him like a blow. He told himself that he would soon get used to the turmoil again. It was surprising how soon a fellow grew countrified.

The doctor's office was his first goal. When the maid ushered him into the consultation room, the great man looked up inquiringly from his card.

"Do you remember me?" Henley Gaither was nervous.

The doctor hesitated.

"I had a Mr. Gaither here last spring," he began, doubtfully.

"Yes. You told me I had six months to live. The time is up."

The physician stared keenly. The face before him was sunburned, with a white line across the forehead. The figure was gaunt, and drooped a little; but there was a promise of sturdiness which weakness could not hide. The doctor rose with decisive interest. "Please take off your coat, Mr. Gaither."

It was a long and thorough examination. Another physician was called in before it ended, and a third. Finally the specialists withdrew to consult. Henley Gaither found himself trembling as he waited for their verdict. He heard their explanations like a man in a dream; but it was not a dream that they told him, "Your trouble is gone; you are practically well. You must be careful for a while, but you are in no danger of dying."

He sat down abruptly, and they laughed and told him that he musn't take the good news that way. They lectured him solemnly about diet and exercise, and prescribed various and sundry rules for every hour of every day.

Then he was out on the street again, and his heart was singing. He was going to live! He was going to live! The joy chanted itself over and over in his mind. He wanted to shout, but there was no place to shout. All about were people, and people, and more people. He wondered, whimsically, what they would do if he were to stand and cry aloud, "I am not dying! I am going to live!"

Just around the corner was his club, where his membership had not yet expired; he would share the good news with some of the fellows.

The doorman looked at him in cold recognition.

"Good morning, Harris. I'm back, you see."

"Yes, sir. Thank you, sir. I hope you are well now, sir." How wooden the man was! But there was inventory in his glance, and for the first time Gaither noticed a frayed edge on his cuff and the irregular crease in his trousers. Aunt Liza had done her best, but she was no tailor.

Old acquaintances nodded to him, but there was no tumult of greeting. He had had few intimate friends; others had lost interest in him.

"What are you doing now?" asked one, carelessly.

"Oh, I've been resting, but I think I'll try to get back into the game now."

"Good thing. Here's luck!" The man moved away with unobtrusive haste. At first Gaither was puzzled; then he remembered how he too had avoided men who had the reputation of being down and out; it was no part of the code to serve as a ladder. They were afraid of him!

He went down to his old offices. Another firm had taken them over, the furniture was changed, and the signs on the doors; but there was the same bustle of eager hurry, the same anxious clatter of typewriters and adding machines, the same rushing of messenger boys, the same hawk-eyed devotion to the Great God Business. He caught his breath; if only he had this organization at his disposal, it wouldn't take him long to put the market under his thumb. Then it would be easy to turn the tables on the Sanderson crowd; they had taken advantage of his partner's flight, but he would beat them single-handed. He wandered in and out of other offices; men greeted him with curt nods. They were the same men who, not a year before, had watched eagerly for the slightest crooking of his finger; now, they had no time for him. Very few asked where he had been, or seemed to know of his illness. Everybody was afraid of him; nobody wanted to be burdened with a climber. He would have to fight it out alone. All right, he could do it; he could fight the whole accursed gang, Sanderson and all, if he wanted to.

When the offices were closing, he bethought himself of the women who had offered themselves for his entertainment in his old hours of leisure. He found a telephone and called a number which had been often on his lips a year before. The voice that answered was soft with studied languor, but it sharpened in recognition.

"Why, Henley Gaither! Where have you been? I thought you must be dead."

"You didn't try very hard to find out, did you, Lilian?"

"How could I, Henley? You simply vanished. Have you come back to stay?"

"Perhaps. I'd like to talk to you a while. How about to-night?"

"To-night? Oh, I'm awfully sorry, but we have some people coming in."

"To-morrow night, then?"

"No, Freddie Holmes is giving a dinner at the Ritz, and we're going afterward to see that new Persian dancer. They say she's fascinatingly improper."

"Well, when am I going to see you?"

"Why, Henley dear, I really don't know. Can't you run away from the office some morning, and take me to lunch? I'll call you one day this week."

"Splendid, only I have no office yet. I am just getting ready to buck the line. I want you to wish me luck."

"Oh, really! Do you mean you are starting in business all over again? How thrilling! It sounds quite like a novel. What are you going to do?"

"Oh, I'll have to start on the ground floor somewhere."

"Well, I truly hope you'll succeed, old thing. But I'd better not ask you to take me to lunch, for you'll be awfully busy, won't you? Maybe I'll run across you somewhere. Oh, here come those people now, and I'm not dressed. Good-by, Henley dear."

Henley Gaither hung up the receiver, and a satirical smile hardened his lips. He called other numbers; and the answers he received were sweet, and careless, and baffling, and final. It certainly took golden bait to catch female fish.

He rambled along Broadway as the theater crowds began to gather. He met people whom he had known well, and they greeted him easily, as if they had seen him only yesterday, and excused themselves promptly and left him. He noticed them looking critically at his clothes.

He found himself tired, and longing for sleep, so he went back to his room. The roar and rattle of the streets pressed in upon him through his opened window, and the air seemed strangely heavy. He couldn't sleep.

He was angry. Nothing had gone as he planned it. The doctors promised him life, and yet there seemed no way to use that life. Nobody wanted him. Well, there was one way to make them want him. When he had built up another fortune, they would run after him, men and women, just as they used to do.

And yet, would it be worth the effort? What was the use of trying to win friends who cared only for what he had? Surely, in all this great city there were multitudes of people who were sincere, and honest, and simple-hearted; but it had not been his luck to find them.

He spurred himself into planning his vengeance on the Sanderson crowd; and in the midst of planning his successful coup, he stopped to wonder if Jim Herndon would remember to water the rose cuttings by the south porch.

He could not sleep. He might have known that people would not welcome him back. They had shown their attitude too plainly last year, but he had not realized it then. No, it would have to be a fight, and fighting was tiresome work, unless there was something to fight for. Of course, there would be a thrill in settling that Sanderson gang; but it would take more capital than he possessed to get started. He might sell Gaither House for enough to start him in the market again—

"No!" His heart fairly shouted the word back at his reason. Sell Gaither House? Why, he couldn't do that! Beating the Sandersons wouldn't be worth while if he had to lose Gaither House to do it. In fact, he really didn't care whether he beat the Sandersons or not. Let them have their old corner! He didn't want to get back into the market. What did it all amount to, anyway?

If that honeysuckle were dug out this fall it would give the violets a chance in the spring. And what was it Ginnie Herndon had said about the strawberry bed?

The Herndons hadn't looked at his clothes. They would have cleaned up his house if he had told them he was coming, and they knew he couldn't pay them for doing it! Ginnie Herndon hadn't snubbed him because he was poor; she had sought him out because he was poor, and sick, and lonely. With the loyal inspiration of a girl like Ginnie Herndon, a man with nothing but his fists could buck the market and knock the Sandersons and all their tribe into Kingdom Come and make millions overnight. And what good would it do him? False, painted moths would flutter to the golden lure—but Ginnie Herndon would rather pick a handful of rosebuds from the bush in the back yard than own all the diamonds in Maiden Lane. He couldn't keep the girl out of his mind.

"I believe I'm in love with Ginnie Herndon," he mocked himself; and then he began to analyze the thought. What else could it be that made him think of her in connection with everything he planned? Of course, she was practically the only female he had seen in months. He had had little conversation with her, except that night before he left, but he had been given almost daily glimpses of her, and their occasional semi-quarrels had revealed her character as hours of parlor-philandering would never have done. She was a wonderfully attractive girl. He decided that he had been in love with her from that first meeting. The seeming antagonism had been the revulsion of his weakness against her pulsing health; envy, and a sense of his own unworthiness to love such splendid vitality had swerved affection into dislike.

But Ginnie would never be happy in the city. For that matter, neither would he—now. He had proven to his full satisfaction the faithlessness of people he had thought he could trust, and association with them could never mean the same again. He was already weary of the dust and confusion and ceaseless noise, and he thought longingly of the restful stillness of Gaither House, with only the twitter of birds and the rustle of wind among the leaves through long lazy hours. He was a country-bred man, and the country was what he had needed all these years; but he had never understood it until now.

He was going home. The train rattled and clattered with something of his own eager desire. He was well, and he was going to be strong, and he was going to be happy. Yes, he could get Liza's nephew to work the plantation this season, while he built up strength in the care of orchard and garden; and by another year he could do it all himself. He would have the old house repaired and freshened. And he would marry Ginnie Herndon.

Then a shocking thought turned his dream into a nightmare. Suppose—just suppose—that Ginnie Herndon might not choose to be married? The Henley Gaither of a year ago would have sneered at such a suggestion. He had been complacently persuaded that he could marry any woman he wanted, if only he showed her money enough. They all had their price. But here was one who apparently had no price. She had shown him innumerable kindnesses, out of pure pity; but he couldn't ask her to marry him out of pity.

His vanity was touched. It was a little hard to admit that he, personally, might have no attraction, that it was only his fortune which had dazzled all those women who had been so willing to say "Yes." Ginnie's manner that night had indicated real interest; but then, she would be really interested in a lost pup. Gaither's pride tumbled headlong as he faced every possibility. He would go to see her right away. If she refused him, it would be a new experience; but he would not give up with the first trial.

The wheels chuckled and crashed their way across the Virginia hills, as if in mockery of his anxiety. Hour after hour he debated, and wondered, and built houses of straw and pulled them down again.

Yet he was strangely happy. He was going to see her anyway, and even if she did not consent refusal from her would be sweeter than acceptance from another woman.

He was a fool. Of course she would refuse. He had nothing to offer her except himself; he was a conceited jackass to think that she would want him. His humiliation was bitter.

It was morning when he reached the little town, and still early morning when the same mud-stained surrey of his first ride deposited him at his own gate. He flung his bags into the porch, and followed the path across the fields towards the Herndon place. He caught a glimpse of Jim Herndon, riding away from a group of cotton pickers. All right, let him go; he wasn't visiting Jim Herndon this time.

Led by a flutter of faded blue gingham, he hurried past the porch and out to the little rock-walled springhouse.

Ginnie, arranging milk crocks on a shelf, gazed at him as if he had been a ghost; then she set the last crock down carefully, and sprang forward with delighted greeting.

"Oh, Mr. Gaither! Mr. Gaither! When did you come back? I'm so glad to see you! What did the doctor say? Do come and sit down, and tell me about it. Are you tired?

"Not a bit," he declared, stoutly. "Yes, I saw the doctors."

"Tell me quick!" Her hand clutched his arm.

"I don't need to; you diagnosed my case before I left," he teased.

Slow comprehension brightened her eyes. "Oh— you mean—you aren't going to die?" She was breathless.

"They say I'll be as well as anybody as soon as I get my strength back." He almost shouted his joy.

"Oh, I'm so glad! I'm so glad! I knew it! Isn't it glorious? But—listen!" Her eyes had shadowed again. "You don't have to go back right away, do you?"

"No. In fact—well, either New York has changed, or I have."

Her eagerness questioned him.

"You know I was counted pretty well-to-do when I lived there, and really I thought I was rather popular. But they made it clear to me this time that they weren't interested in me at all. As long as they thought they could get something out of me, I was a good fellow; but as soon as they found out I was poor, they had no more use for me than for a yellow dog."

Her eyes blazed indignation, but she did not speak.

"And the everlasting racket got on my nerves. I reckon I'm just a rube after all." Bitterness had overmastered his desire.

"I'd rather be a million rubes than be selfish and unprincipled enough to hurt a friend just because he had lost a little money!" The vehemence of her outburst startled him into hope.

He must tell her; but words fled from his tongue. It had been easy enough to talk light nothings to the women whose flattering attention promised assent to the question they wanted him to ask, but now that he had found the whole desire of his heart he could not put his hunger into speech.

"I thought once I'd stay and win another fortune," he began, hesitatingly. "But I decided that it wasn't worth while, and I couldn't get interested in those people anyway, but I just had to come back here, because—oh, Ginnie, can't you understand?"

Voice and eyes interpreted the blundering question. As the girl realized its import, swift color flushed her cheeks but her direct gaze did not falter.

"You see, Ginnie, all my life I've needed something, but I didn't know what it was until I went back to New York and found how lonely I was for you. I need you over at Gaither House; I need you to make it really my House of Life."

For a long moment she was silent, and slowly she turned away.

"Ginnie, dear?" His whole heart was in the plea.

She looked up in shy confusion, and then her timid hands fluttered out to meet his.

THE HOUSE OF LONELINESS

BY

MRS. J. BRYAN GRIMES

———

Awarded the Separk Cup in 1923

THE HOUSE OF LONELINESS

O little, lonely house, that stands
Beside the quiet way;
Within your tangled garden spot,
No happy children play.
Your empty windows only show
The twilight's gathering glooms,
And ghosts of long dead happiness
Flit in your silent rooms.

O little, lonely, lonely house,
It hurts my heart to see
Such gray and aching dreariness,
Where love and life should be.
Your open doors hold shadows
For broken hopes to hide,
Your hearth is like an empty heart
Where love has long since died.

O little, lonely house grown gray,
With passing yesteryears,
The sound of love and laughter
Should greet my listening ears,
The ring of happy voices,
Of lullabies crooned low,
And from your gleaming windows shine,
The firelight's welcome glow.

O little, lonely, silent house,
Beneath your brooding eaves,
The nesting birds should sing their songs
Amid the whisp'ring leaves,
And down your fragrant garden paths,
Gay childish feet should roam.
O little, lonely, lonely house,
That once meant love and home.

SUCH A LITTLE BIT O' BABY

BY

DAISY M. HENDLEY

Entered in the 1923 Contest

SUCH A LITTLE BIT O' BABY

Little blue-eyed baby
  A-peeking through the gate,
You're watching for somebody
  Who loves to see you wait
In little checkered apron
  To match your eyes with blue;
No wonder in this world
  Is like the innocence of you—
Such a little bit o' baby
  In gingham apron blue.

Little sweet-lipped baby
  A-talking as you wait,
What mysteries you speak of
  A-peeking through the gate!
The world is wonderful beyond
  The bars you're peeping through,
The world is wonderful as seen
  By those bright eyes of you—
Such a little bit o' baby
  In gingham apron blue.

THEY'S LIARS HERE

BY

JOY KIME BENTON

———

Awarded the O. Henry Cup in 1923

THEY'S LIARS HERE

KEWPIE-DEAR Tuck was dressing for church. She preened her small self, like a vain peacock, before a bit of mirror which hung on the cabin wall.

Here, however, the resemblance ended. Kewpie-dear Tuck looked much more like some strange, freakish cross-breed of barnyard fowl. Her small, round head with its crop of "tight-wropped" pigtails was surmounted by a huge rakish bow of soiled white ribbon. This gave the upper part of her body the look of a pert Houdan hen. Her bandy legs terminated in slippers noticeable both for their behemothian size and their startling color. They were of that indescribable mixture of yellow and red which no mortal eye has beheld elsewhere on sea or land, save in the shoes darkies of Southern plantations have a penchant for, and get goodness knows where. These slippers were adorned with bows of the brightest scarlet scarcely less in size than the one topping her head. This gave Kewpie-dear's lower extremeties a look ludicrously suggestive of an eccentric Shanghai rooster.

Through the open door of the lean-to, Malinda Tuck, Kewpie-dear's mother, regarded her strutting offspring with troubled eyes. Malinda's children all bore "quality" names, which they obligingly lived up to with the exception of Kewpie-dear. She gave Malinda more concern than did all the others. The three boys in the family were: Major, Lawyer, and Judge Tuck respectively. They had been named for some member of the Shirley family who lived in the "big house" on the hill, beginning with Judge Shirley's grandfather who had been a major in the Confederate army, and ending with the Judge, himself.

The girls were: Ivory Fairy, named from a combination of two highly-colored magazine advertisements which with others adorned the cabin walls in lieu of wall-paper, and Kewpie-dear whom Mrs. Shirley, herself, had named.

When the last named baby was only a few days old, Mrs. Shirley had gone from the "big house" on the hill to the cabin to carry Malinda a basket of delicacies. Little Margaret Shirley had accompanied her mother to see the new piccaninny and had lingered in the yard to watch Ivory Fairy in the interesting process of braiding her long, straight hair into many fascinating little braids. Ivory Fairy's hair was a heritage from her father, Brookshire Tuck, who had Indian blood in his veins. Margaret was absorbed in watching the nimble brown fingers weave in and out when her mother called her.

"Come in and see the Kewpie, dear."

Margaret went hastily to view the small, tan baby just out of its bath and still wearing "birthday" clothes.

"Whut dat name yo' done specify, Mis' Ellen?" Malinda asked, as she deftly slipped a nondescript garment over the baby's head.

"Why, Kewpie, Malinda. Haven't you seen those cute, little, roly-poly dolls? Kewpies, they call them. This baby looks just like one with her big, bright eyes and plump, round tummy."

"No'm, Mis' Ellen! Dat ain't de way yo' spoke hit de fust time; yo' say: 'Kewpie-deah.' Yas'm, dat de way yo' spoke hit."

"Oh," Mrs. Shirley laughed, "I was speaking to Margaret!"

"*Kewpie-deah, Kewpie-deah,*" Malinda nodded positively. "Yas'm, dat whut I gwine call dis-heah chile. Dat gwine be her 'title-ment sho'."

As Kewpie-dear grew older she lost her Kewpish rotundity. Her cream color deepened quickly into claybank then chocolate brown, which in turn gave way to a black so deep and lustrous that she resembled nothing so much as an audacious poster done in very black ink.

From the first she was a vain little thing, decking herself in whatever finery she could lay her hands on. The Shirley girls, delighting in the startling effects she could achieve, gave her bits of ribbon and lace and other discarded finery. Once one of them contributed a boudoir cap. It was of lace, ribbon, and rosebuds, and had been a dainty thing but now the pristine freshness was only a memory. This was Kewpie-dear's most cherished treasure, kept for state occasions. To her mind it was the hallmark of gentility, for didn't the "quality" wear them? And, too, it concealed the numerous, humiliating, "wropped" pigtails that radiated from her small head Kewpie-dear's one great sorrow was her hair. A sorrow that bit deeper each time Ivory Fairy combed her straight black locks within sight of Kewpie-dear's envious eyes.

This Thursday afternoon Malinda, as she finished "riddin'" up the lean-to and started redecorating the cabin walls by pasting fresh copies of the "Carolina Banner" over the newspapers already there, sighed and sighed again. This evening a joint revival of Methodists and Baptists was beginning at the Dry Ark Chapel; and the responsibility for Kewpie-dear's soul weighed heavily on Malinda's heart. All the other children had by the time they reached nine years of age "been to de moaner's bench an' got religion an' jined." Three of them were in the Methodist fold with their father, Brookshire Tuck, and two had been baptized in the faith of the Baptist church, of which Malinda was an ardent member. Kewpie-dear alone remained unsaved.

For the past twelve months she had been the bone of contention in the Tuck cabin and between the two churches. At both Methodist and Baptist meetings she had been preached to, prayed at, exhorted, and admonished; but in the end she had not been turned from the ways "ob de flesh inter de fold ob de sperit." Kewpie-dear, when it came to matters of religion, for a reason she kept in her own small head, remained adamantine and unmoved.

Now, as she dressed for church, she alternately removed the huge white bow, replaced it with the

boudoir cap, and vice versa. She had about made a
final decision in favor of the bow when Malinda's
voice broke in upon her absorption.

"Kewpie-deah," the voice was impatient, "how-come
yo' ain't ready for meetin' yit?"

Kewpie-dear leisurely removed the bow and replaced
it with the cap. Then she answered.

"I *is* ready, Mammy. I's jest starting out to de
carryall dis minute."

"Carryall, nothin'! Yo' ain't gwine ride in no carryall! Yo' gwine hoof it 'longside ob me an' Iv'ry Fai'y.
Yo' pappy been makin' loud-mouf brags 'bout how he
gwine git de las' whack at yo' on de way to de meetin'
house, an' I sho' pintedly gwine break up his playhouse.
Him an' dem triflin' boys can go an' ride in de carryall, but I gwine take yo' an' Iv'ry Fai'y an' hoof it de
whole endurin' way. No Mef'dis' nigger gwine put
nuffin over on me; no suh! When yo' git religiom,
chile, I sho' gwine see dat yo' gits de Babdis' bran'.'"

Kewpie-dear smoothed the ends of the resplendent
yellow sash she wore, and looked longingly at the
carryall wherein sat Brookshire and the three boys.
But she obediently followed Malinda and Ivory Fairy
out of the door and down the fresh-swept path to the
gate. Here she paused and, sitting down, removed her
shoes and stockings, wriggling her liberated black toes
ecstatically in the cool white sand. Then she arose,
took the discarded articles of wearing apparel in her
hand, and trailed along after her mother and sister.

It was a good mile to the Dry Ark Chapel, and when
they came in sight of its weather-beaten roof, Kewpie-

dear sat down and put on her shoes and stockings. This accomplished, she carefully dusted the former on the latter by the simple expedient of rubbing them up and down on the calves of her skinny legs.

When they reached the chapel, they were joined by Brookshire and the boys, who, having preceded them and unharnessed and fed old Jill beneath a large oak tree, were now loitering around the door.

Major, the oldest boy, to all intents and purposes was absorbed in something that was taking place near the side of the church. He stood still and stared interestedly around the corner of the church. Malinda, at last unable to restrain her curiosity, edged toward him and before she realized what was afoot, Brookshire, taking advantage of the temporary lifting of her vigilence, seized Kewpie-dear by the hand and whisked her through the open door. Still holding her hand he clumped up the aisle and plumped her down on the front seat of the "men's side" which had been set apart for the Methodists.

Malinda, discomfited, with blood in her eye, waddled in and took a seat on the "women's side," or the side reserved for the Baptists; the grinning Ivory Fairy sauntering along behind.

The small room was filled to overflowing. Saints and sinners alike filled benches and windows. The loud buzz of conversation preceding the sermon was interspersed with yet louder bursts of laughter. But a temporary hush followed the entrance of the Tuck family, as there had been much speculation as to where the unsaved Kewpie-dear would sit. Each church hoped to "git de fust whack" at her, there being a tacit understanding that on which ever side a sinner elected to sit, that side should have the privilege of first approaching him or her, as the case might be, as to his or her soul's salvation. So on the Methodist side a pleased murmur ran over the congregation, and white teeth blossomed broadcast, while on the Baptist side there was disgruntled silence.

Then the Reverend Sherman Corn, Baptist, accompanied by the Reverend Crater Belcher, Methodist, entered and walked up the aisle bowing pompously each to his respective congregation. And as they mounted the platform that served as a pulpit a voice somewhere in the congregation started a song.

> "Heaven . . . Hea-ven
> Everybody talk about Heaven don't go there,"

the melodious voice trilled.

> "Heaven . . . Heaven!"

echoed a pure tenor voice from the rear.

Then the Methodist congregation joined in:

> "I got shoes, you got shoes,
> *All* God's chillun got shoes
> Gwine put on my shoes, dey fits me so well,
> Gwine walk *all round* God's Heaven.
> Y-e-s, it is a Hea-ven . . ."

Kewpie-dear, sitting on the front bench, raised her voice in tuneful melody and rocked in ecstacy as she sang. Her song came, not from any overflow of religious feeling, but from the welling forth of a supreme gift given to the negro race; the gift of melody. She lifted her head and sang as a bird might sing. From time to time she reached down and, with a colorful silk handkerchief which she produced from the heel of her right shoe, meticulously dusted and polished her amazing footwear.

> "They's li-ars heah, they's li-ars theah,
> They's li-ars ev-er-y where; Jesus Lawd, He do declare
> They'll be no li-ars theah . . . in Heaven, Hea-ven.
> Everybody talk about Heaven don't go theah.
> Heaven! Yes it is a Heaven . . ."

Singing and swaying back and forth with increasing fervor, the entire congregation now sang. The sixth stanza was well under way when, from the amen corner, a brother rose singing lustily, advanced to the pulpit, and dropped a small coin into a hat which was conveniently upturned on a table. Then another rose, and yet another, until the entire church was a mass of chanting, rythmic humanity.

Kewpie-dear untied from one corner of the colorful handkerchief, five pennies. She marched importantly up, deposited one penny, and resumed her seat. After a few moments she personally conducted the second penny to the hat, and so on until the five had been placed therein. Throughout the church other singers changed dimes and quarters into coins of smaller denominations so that the trip up the aisle might be made with much ostentation again and again.

Then the Reverend Sherman Corn arose, adjusted what looked suspiciously like a huge pair of automobile goggles, peered through them earnestly and said:

"Bref-ren an' Sis-tren, Ah takes fo' ma tex' de latterly part of de epistle ob de Opossum Maffew: 'I-i-if ye hab faith as a grain of mustard seed, ye shall say unto dis-heah mount'n, be ye remove a-a-an' hit shall remove.' A-a-all yo' folkses a-a-settin' hard in de amen corner; A-all yo' peoples a-restin' yeasy on de yudder benches, listen to dem gran' words, Lis'en to dat golden promise. Y'all want somethin', de whole worl' want somethin', an' de good Book, hit say, all yo' got to do is *ax an' believe*.

"De Lawd done sont a train, de train ob faith. All yo' got do is to git on hit an' ride straight down de track to de lan' where de things yo' desires is a-hangin' on de trees. Ax an' believe, and den sit back on de gospel cyars an' watch de wheels cicumocute."

"*A-men, Brudder!*" a voice from the amen corner bellowed.

"Yo' done spoke de trufe," another echoed.

"Bress de Lawd, I'se a-runnin' fo' de deepo now!" still another sang out. And a sister back on the Methodist side started shouting.

But Kewpie-dear Tuck sat unheedful of these things. She stared open-mouthed at the preacher. The words he had just uttered were interesting; they cast a new light on religion. If *that* was what religion meant she certainly had been missing something! Well, it was not too late. She wanted something and she would ask the Lord for it now. She would ask Him to *straighten her hair,* and when He had done so she would seek forthwith the "moaner's bench." So she closed her eyes and said her little prayer trustingly, deciding as she did so that she would wait until the sermon was over to view the miracle. She would give the Lord plenty of time to attend to the matter in case He should be busy with some one else's prayer when she asked.

After what seemed an age, the Reverend Sherman Corn ended his sermon and called upon Brookshire Tuck to lead them in a word of prayer. Kewpie-dear, who had fidgeted uneasily throughout the sermon, now produced from the folds of her resplendent sash, a small mirror. Cautiously she raised the edge of the boudoir cap and surveyed her head. Her lips quivered pathetically, a sob rose in her throat, and two clear, round tears rolled slowly down her polished cheeks. For under the cap where she had expected to see a mass of smooth, shining hair, the hated pigtails still bristled tauntingly. A great wave of anger swept her soul. What the preacher had said was not true! She had been deceived, cruelly deceived!

It was at this inopportune moment that a good Methodist sister, seeing tears and mistaking them for tears of repentance, approached Kewpie-dear in regard to saving her soul.

"Go 'way nigger!" said Kewpie-dear, shrilly. "Go 'way wid yo' lies. De Lawd whut can't take time fo to straighten ma ha'r, ain't gwine fool no time wid savin' ma soul. *Go 'way from heah!*"

Straightway up rose Malinda from the Baptist congregation and steered a course to the culprit's side. Taking her by the ear she shook her soundly.

"How-come yo' speak out dat-a-way an' disgrace yo' bringings up? I gwine teach yo' to projic' wid de word of de Lawd. I gwine . . ."

"Praise de Lawd!" a voice at Malinda's elbow shouted. "Praise Gawd! He done call me to be his agent. He done spoke to me. He say: 'Pi-ano Shanks, I got work fo' yo' to commit. Minister to Sistah Kewpie-deah Tuck.' He say: 'De white folks, dey heats an iron an' makes straight hair curly; usin' de same instrumentation, I 'structs yo' to heat an iron an' officiate to de young sistah. Hit a poor rule dat won't work bofe ways'."

Then up rose the Methodist congregation. Cries of "git de iron!" "minister to de young sistah," "do de Lawd's will!" and similar exclamations sounded from all sides.

Willing hands soon started a fire in the small, rusty stove. Some one rummaged around and produced a broken screw-driver which they heated. Then Piano Shanks, the ambassador, advanced to where Kewpie-dear Tuck sat palpitating between fright and anticipation.

Finally the great longing in Kewpie-dear's heart overcame her fear. With fingers that trembled she removed the boudoir cap, unwound one of the "wropped" pigtails and offered it to the waiting Piano. There was a sharp cry; a smell of burning wool; a swift movement; and Kewpie-dear had vanished through the door, leaving the wispy remains of what had been a black pigtail in the hands of the amazed Piano.

Sobbing with pain and mortification, she ran, never stopping until she had reached the cabin. Here she crawled under the bed, and when the family returned from church they found her there asleep.

The following morning Malinda went about her work with sombre eyes. Kewpie-dear's chance for the Kingdom seemed slipping away. In her heart Malinda rejoiced at the Methodist fiasco. If the Baptists *only could* find a way. *If only they could!* Often during the morning she beat upon her ample breast and groaned aloud. If only *she* could find a way!

Perhaps if she sat down and thought, and thought, something might come to her. She sat down.

"Huh," she murmured after a while, "feel lack I gwine see a vision . . . feels mahself approachin' into a trance."

Swaying slightly back and forth, head bent a little forward, eyes roving blankly over the cabin wall, she sat, and from time to time uttered soft, incoherent, crooning noises.

Suddenly her eyes lost their blankness. A look of deepest curiosity filled them. Something on the cabin wall caught and held her attention. She started at a spot which in turn became a spot no longer but a message. The Lord had answered her prayer; He was telling her what to do!

Looking cautiously around her, Malinda rose, approached the wall and scrutinized it carefully. Fully fifteen minutes she gave it her earnest attention. Then she took a keen-bladed knife and with careful hand removed a small portion of the newspaper she had pasted there the day before. Looking furtively around her she folded the bit of paper, and muttering strange incantations, bent and placed it in her left shoe. As Brookshire and the children came up the path, she hastily resumed her seat in the trance attitude, head slightly bent, eyes staring vacantly. And when the children swarmed into the room followed by their father, Malinda rose with a shout.

"Bress de Lawd!" she began in the good old way. "Bress His name! I'm done seen a visiom; He done show me a miracle. He done spoke to old black Lindy wif de voice of a trump. He say: 'Malinda, they's liars here; they's liars here in the midst of de congregation of de opposin'. De devil been tryin' to ac' as my 'bassador. Yistiddy in de church he done spoke to Pi-ano Shanks an' 'tice her to projec' with an' tant'lize dat bressed chile, Kewpie-deah.' De Lawd say: 'Malinda, *you's* de agent I's a-callin'; *you's* de meejum by which I desires Kewpie-deah gathered into de fold. De fire ob de Mefodis' ain't gwine save her, but de water ob de Babdis' will.' He say: 'Listen whiles I give yo' special instructums.'

" 'Yo' go,' de Lawd specify, 'on de comin' Sunday mornin' to de Goose Creek babdizin' hole an' in de presence ob two witnesses dip two cups full ob de water, pour hit in a bottle an' fetch it home.' He say: 'When Kewpie-deah done said her prayers ev'ry night, rub some ob de water on her ha'r den put de boo-door cap on her haid an', 'ceptance de times yo' takes hit off to minister to her head, keep it dar 'twell de day comes fo' yo' to remove hit in de presence ob de congregation.' " Malinda paused for breath, then added, "He done say, too, if'n she peek one time at her hair afore de appointed time comes, den He not gwine make hit straight a-tall."

During this recital Kewpie-dear's eyes had grown large and round and wistful.

"Mammy," she said, "I done tried de Lawd out two times. He ain't got no time to fool wid a little cullud girl a-tall."

"Honey," said Malinda, earnestly, "de Lawd *sho'* gwine give yo' yo' desiahment. Jes' take yo' ole mammy's word fo' hit dis time."

The following morning Malinda, reassuring herself that the precious bit of paper was safe in her shoe, prepared for the weekly trip to the nearby town of Cameron. All dressed in her starched Sunday best, she climbed over the wheel of the carryall where Brookshire sat waiting, and they moved off. Brookshire drove the entire distance there and back in gloomy silence; but Malinda broke often into joyous song.

Sunday morning, bright and early, Malinda went by a neighboring cabin, got her two witnesses, and all proceeded to the baptizing hole. Here Malinda followed faithfully the instructions as she had spoken them two days before. She dipped two cupfuls of the water, poured them into a bottle, and returned with the bottle to the cabin. She did not attend meeting that day, but sang around the cabin, interspersing her songs with spells of shouting.

When bedtime came the cabin was filled with visitors. The account of Malinda's vision had travelled fast, and curious darkies hastened to the Tuck cabin to see the beginning of this miracle.

Kewpie-dear had been undressed early and she sat in a gay old kimona waiting.

With great solemnity, Malinda produced a bottle. She removed the huge white bow from Kewpie-dear's kinky head, unwrapped the tight little pigtails, tilted the bottle and began to pour. When the woolly mass was throughly saturated, she laid her hands caressingly on the child's head and gently rubbed. Then she took from a box a curious looking comb and used it diligently.

Night after night this performance was repeated; Malinda rolling her eyes and quoting verses of scripture; Kewpie-dear, her small black face all large wistful eyes, submitting uncomplainingly. After the first night, though, the whole performance was carried on without witnesses; but always Kewpie-dear was admonished not to, under any circumstances, remove the carefully adjusted boudoir cap.

Finally came the day of days—the Sabbath that had been elected for the public removal of the boudoir cap.

Early in the morning, in the seclusion of the lean-to, Malinda gave Kewpie-dear's head her final ministrations. Kewpie-dear was then dressed in her bravest attire—yellow shoes with new red bows, blue dress, resplendent sash, and the now harrassed-looking boudoir cap. This time she did not walk to church, but climbed over the wheel of the carryall and took her seat in a little straight-backed chair beside Malinda. All the way to church she sat very still, her eyes wistful with expectation.

At the Dry Ark Chapel a crowd had gathered, Methodists and Baptists alike. They had come from miles around. Some skeptically loquacious, others loquacious but with fullest faith.

Malinda and the Reverend Sherman Corn drew aside and conversed earnestly for a few moments in subdued tones. Then the Reverend Corn mounted the pulpit.

"Bref-ren an' sis-tren," he began. "We-all is gathered here to see sistah Kewpie-dear Tuck start trablin' on de gospel cyars. She's at de deepo ob de sperit now, an' a-gittin' her qualifumcations ready fo' to mount de platform." He paused. "All at's been standin' betwix dis beloved sistern and de fold, is onbelief. She 'low dat ef'n de Lawd could'nt taken de time to straighten her ha'r, den he wouldn't be botherationed none wif de matter ob her soul. Bref-ren an' sis-tren! De Lawd done heard her pra'r. He done delivered her from her onbelief, an' now I's gwine show yo' de resultment ob de miracle. Sistah Kewpie-deah Tuck, step forwards."

Kewpie-dear and Malinda got up. As they stepped forward, Piano Shanks, with seeming artlessness, started a song. From somewhere in the rear of the Methodist congregation, a male voice joined in. It was the voice of Brookshire Tuck.

"Hea-ven . . . Hea-ven . . .
Everybody talk about Heaven don't go there . . .
Hea-ven . . ."

The song was interrupted by the Reverend Sherman Corn who raised an impressive hand for silence. He advanced to the edge of the pulpit and assisted Kewpie-dear to mount.

"Sistah Malindy Tuck, will yo' kindly step up on de platforms an' 'sist wid de comin' ceremonious?" he invited.

Putting out his hand he helped her up and the three of them faced the congregation.

"Frien's," he began, "I axes yo' all to behold an' stand testimony to dis great happenance. De good book hit say ax an' believe an' hit shall be did unto yo'. Dis-heah sistah done ax an' believe an' de Lawd done heard her prayer. Now we gwine demonstrate to yo' de resultment of de miracle, an' 'ceive her into de Babdis' fold. Sistah Tuck, I commands yo' to remove de cap!"

Malinda cast a superior eye over the faces before her, moved importantly forward, put out her hand, paused for a dramatic moment . . . then lifted the cap.

A murmur of astonishment ran through the congregation. Necks were craned; eyes grew large. Kewpie-dear stood demurely before them, smiling happily. Her short hair was parted in the exact middle of her head, and was drawn down over her ears in two shining scallops . . . smooth, sleek and satiny.

Malinda swept the congregation with triumphant eye. Then looking meaningly at the astonished Piano Shanks, she started the *second* stanza of the song which Piano had begun a short while before.

> "They's li-ars here, they's li-ars there,
> They's li-ars every where—"

Late that night after the Tuck family was safely asleep, Malinda, sitting in the firelight, reached and cautiously took from her shoe a bit of paper. Unfolding it, she read for the last time:

"Try Mrs. Annex's Hair Straightener. Guaranteed to invigorate and straighten the coarsest and kinkiest hair. For sale by the Cameron Drug Company."

"De Lawd he'ps dem dat he'ps demselves," Malinda chuckled. She tore the paper into tiny bits and dropped them on the glowing coals.

BILL AN' ME

BY

ELLA H. LACKEY

Entered in 1923 Contest

BILL AN' ME

When Bill an' me crawl in our bed,
Maw tucks the quilts from foot to head,
An' when she carries out the light,
An' shets us in, as black as night,
The things what lame Unk tells to us,
That ketches boys what swear and cuss,
Sich spooks an' things you never see,
Come peekin' in at Bill an' me.

Now pap, he sez they ain't no sich,
They ain't no spooks an' ain't no witch,
But Unk, he tells us orful tales
Of folks what uster swaller whales,
An' witches ridin' on a broom,
An' noises walkin' 'bout the room,
An' things with eyes what we can't see,
A lookin' after Bill an' me.

One night when Unk an' Bill an' me
Went down by that ol' chestnut tree,
Where crazy Sal took suicide,
An' walks the same as 'fore she died,
Ole Unk, he led his 'possum houn'
What had black spots, an' white an' brown—
'Twuz dark as pitch, an' cloudy, gee!
We wuz some scared, wuz Bill an' me.

'N' 'en Unk, he turns his ol' houn loose,
So's he kin fin' the 'possum roos';
'N' 'en in the swamp we see a light
Go up an' down, 'n' 'en outer sight,
'N' 'en come ag'in, without no han's,
A Jack O' Lantern—my good lan's!
The houn' dawg run for the 'simmon tree,
An' Unk outrun both Bill and me.

MY BABY

BY
SALLIE STEWART NIEMYER

Entered in the 1923 Contest

MY BABY

While looking at the picture of my baby four years old,
I remember when he marched to war with wooden gun
    so bold;
His little eyes with brilliance shone, his voice was
    deep and grand,
And, like a captain brave and true, he shouted this
    command:
"Hep, hep, keep step, soldiers, to the band;
We're going to fight the giants in the foreign country
    land."

The back yard was his battlefield, the china tree his
    tent,
Tho' all alone, he'd "make believe" he drilled a regi-
    ment.
He'd forward march, then call a halt, and at attention
    stand,
Then give the order, "Forward, march!" and wave his
    mighty hand.
"Hep, hep, keep step, soldiers, to the band;
We're going to fight the giants in the foreign country
    land."

Pretending that I wept, I said, "Oh, son, do not
    depart;
If giants kill the soldier boy, 'twould break his mother's
    heart!"
He said, "Don't cry, dear mother; I'm strong and
    brave, you see;
I'll kill them all, then march back home; then see how
    proud you'll be."
"Hep, hep, keep step, soldiers, to the band;
We're going to fight the giants in the foreign country
    land."

His baby days have passed away; to manhood he has
  grown;
He answers now his country's call, and childhood
  plays are done;
For ere the Germans, fierce and bold, oppressed us
  on the sea,
He joined the U. S. Army, a soldier brave to be.
"Hep, hep, keep step, soldiers, to the band;
We're going to fight the giants in the foreign country
  land."

Once more I said, while weeping, "Oh, son, do not
  depart;
If Germans killed this soldier boy, 'twould break his
  mother's heart!"
With tear-dimmed eyes and trembling voice, my baby
  said to me,
"I'm strong and brave; I'll come back home; but
  mother pray for me."
"Hep, hep, keep step, soldiers, to the band;
We're going to fight the giants in the foreign country
  land."

And now, oh, God! he kept his word; he's gone with
  gun in hand,
To fight the cruel giants in the foreign country land.
The ocean is his battlefield, a big ship is his tent,
His wooden gun is changed for steel that shoots thro'
  firmament.
"Hep, hep, keep step, soldiers, to the band;
He's gone to fight the giants in the foreign country
  land."

THE MOONSTONE

BY

MRS. AL FAIRBROTHER

Entered in the 1923 Contest

THE MOONSTONE

'Twas moonlight on the ocean
The tide was running high,
And the sirens all were singing
To the winds their lullaby,
Then the little Neppies gathered
For a frolic in the foam,
For, like the fairies of the land,
Night is their time to roam.
It was a merry party this—
These children of the sea;
They laughed and danced as billows rolled
In wildest revelry.
Then one proposed a contest game
Of bubbles blown ashore—
Bubbles from the frothy waves
Of ocean's endless store,
And from their hidden ocean beds
The toughest straws they drew,
And every fairy in his turn
A wondrous bubble blew.

When, at the dawn, the fairies fled,
A joyous, careless band,
These eerie things unknown to men
Lay white upon the sand:
White from fear of human gaze—
These strangers on the strand,
Torn rudely from their mother's breast
And cast upon the land.

From perils vague of earth and air
They tried in vain to hide
Amid the sands that sheltered them
In lonely desert wide.
But when the herald, purple clad,
Proclaimed the God of Day,
These timid little ocean waifs
Were blinded by the ray.
The burst of light had dazzled them
And chilled them to the bone—
The bold kiss of the rising sun
Had turned them into stone.

*   *   *   *

And this is how we find them—
With the moonbeams sifting through;
With the glint of early morning
And the crust of frost and dew.
This is the simple story
Of the Moonstone's doubtful light,
Which had its birth at the fairy dance
On that wild and fateful night.

THE PRODIGALS

BY

MISS MARY E. WELLS

Entered in the 1923 Contest

THE PRODIGALS

THE TRAIN which had been creeping up the eastern slope of the Blue Ridge seemed to take new vigor as it started down the western side. Two young men were standing on the platform of the Blue Crest flag station watching its retreat.

"The blamed thing seems glad to be rid of us. It hasn't moved with that much pep all day."

"Well, now that it's gone we might as well get acquainted with our new surroundings," rejoined his companion.

"It won't take long to do that. The only living creature here seems to be yon solitary buzzard. He may make our acquaintance sooner than we wish. A few nights on the mountain with neither food nor shelter, and he will be feasting on our carcasses."

"Pshaw now,· Sam, there's no use taking it so hard. Perhaps you've forgotten that we're not exactly on a pleasure trip. Our leaving college just two months before graduation was not so much a desire to travel as it was to avoid an invitation to do so, and our destination was determined by the first train out of town and the condition of our finances rather than choice. In fact, our one idea was to get just as far from the old Dean as possible. And now we're here we might as well make the best of it. Do you suppose there's a human habitation within twenty miles where we can secure supper and lodging for the night?"

"No, I don't, and if there were we haven't any money, and I've no intention of begging."

"Come, Sam, cheer up. Perhaps you wish you'd stayed to face the faculty and be sent home in disgrace."

"Disgrace is bad enough, but starvation is worse. Anyhow, how did we know we'd be fired?"

"How did we know? Possibly you remember that this is our third scrape. The first time we escaped because your dad is a preacher and the old Dean couldn't bear to bring sorrow to the profession."

"Oh, shut up!"

"Yes, I'm going to. The second time the intercollegiate debate saved us. You were the only hope to win. This time there was nothing. The faculty has long thought that it could spare me even though I was a leader of the college songs and yells. But come, let's hunt a cave if you object to a farm house. It's growing late."

"See here, Jim, we planned to go as far as our money would take us and then get a job. All right so far, but what sort of a job can we get here?"

"Well, I don't know unless it's cracking nuts for the squirrels. But, look! What is that coming? Ye Gods, a wagon!"

A canvas covered conveyance drew up alongside the platform and a tall, thin man, wearing a suit of gray homespun, hailed them.

"Wal, now I reckon you be the fellers I'm a lookin' fer. Jist hand up your baggage and climb right in. Had ye give me out comin'?"

"Oh, no," stammered Jim, "we thought you'd be along soon. We were just looking around a bit while we waited."

"Wal, I'm glad ye didn't give me out." And turning his mules around, he started back up the road. "We'll jist about git home by dark. 'Taint more'n eight mile and a man can easy drive three mile an hour and not hurry much either. But, which of you is the preacher? Le's see, Ashton was the name the letter said, I believe."

"Yes," said Jim. "Ashton's right. This is the Reverend Ashton," placing his hand on Sam's shoulder and at the same time giving him a kick on the shin.

"Wal, now I sure am glad to make your acquaintance, and you'rn, too," turning to Jim. "I do believe they done forgot to tell your name."

"My name is Kates, James Kates," volunteered Jim.

"Wal, I reckon you know me. I'm Tom Gibson."

"Yes, I supposed you were," said Jim. "It's mighty good of you to come for us."

"Oh, I didn't mind. I always like to help a good thing along, an' it's been quite a spell since we've had a revival at Dark Ridge. We ain't never had a feller to lead the singing before. But you see, Mary, she's my daughter, and plays the orgin, she says down whar she's been to school they alwa's has someone like that, so she would have to get one for the meetin'. You look mighty young. Have ye been preachin' long?"

"No," replied Sam. "You see I haven't been out of college but a short time."

[243]

9

"Wal, you'll jist have to wade right in, fer ye see, the devil's got a pretty strong holt up Dark Ridge way. The preachers we've had fer the last three or four year ain't been able to stir up much excitement."

After more than two hours of bumping over the rocky road, Mr. Gibson stopped his mules in front of a one-story log house, and called out, "Hello thar, Ma, here we be," and Mrs. Gibson, wiping her hands on the gingham apron, came to welcome her guests.

"Come right in," she said, "I know you're hungry. You'll find soap and water on the back porch. Mary, bring a fresh towel. I'll dish supper while you get ready. There's a comb right under the lookin' glass."

She disappeared into the kitchen and as the young men were preparing to make their toilet, a girl of seventeen brought a fresh towel and arranged it on the roller. She seemed timid and barely spoke to the strangers. Her task finished, she slipped back into the house.

"Jim", said Sam as he washed the train dust from his face, "Jim!" Getting no reply, he turned to find Jim gazing at the open door. "Jim," he said, slapping him on the back, "what ails you?"

"Gosh, did you see that!"

"See what?"

"Did you see that hair and those eyes, and that wonderful color?"

"Boy, for heaven's sake, come to. A nice mess this!"

"This? Oh, this is heaven. A good supper and a bed to sleep in after anticipating a bunk on the ground with a rock pillow, and Starvation for a bed-fellow; let alone being food for buzzards. For once the Fates are kind."

"Jim, when we left college, I swore that you had got me into my last scrape. Now here we are again."

"Again? Why, this is real Providence. Here we are saved from a sad and early grave and placed in the way of making money."

"What do you mean, Jim?"

"Well, you *are* stupid! Don't the preacher always take a collection at the close of a revival, a sort of free-will offering, we might say?"

"Jim, you are crazy. There'll be no revival."

Mr. Gibson came around the corner of the house just in time to hear the last remark.

"See here, young preacher, ye ain't a gittin' out o' heart, air ye?"

"Oh, no," stammered Sam, "but I don't see where the people will come from. I didn't see many houses along the road."

"Don't ye worry about the crowd. It'll be there all right, as soon as ye git sot in. But supper's ready. . . . Preacher, you say grace. . . Now jist help yourselves."

Never did two hungrier boys devour fried chicken, Irish potatoes, corn-bread and buttermilk.

After supper they all sat around the log fire and talked until bedtime.

"Preacher," said Mr. Gibson, "won't you read and pray? Mary, set the lamp on the stand over thar by the preacher and git the Bible."

Sam, embarrassed, opened the Bible and turned page after page without finding anything appropriate or familiar. Jim, watching uneasily, at last came to the rescue.

"Instead of reading to-night," he said, "why can't we each repeat a selection from the Bible and then have the Lord's Prayer?"

The new plan met with approval and Mr. Gibson led off with a few verses from the Prophecy of Isaiah. Mrs. Gibson followed with a selection from the Psalms. Mary modestly added a single verse. Jim, looking at the pretty face opposite him, said earnestly:

"Entreat me not to leave thee, nor to return from following after thee: for whither thou goest, I will go; and where thou lodgest, I will lodge: thy people shall be my people, and thy God my God."

And now it was Sam's turn, but in vain he tried to think of one single verse. At last he murmured, " 'Jesus wept'. Let us join in the Lord's Prayer," and kneeling by his chair, he started, "The Lord is my shepherd, I shall not—." But at this moment Jim gave a warning kick which missed Sam's bended knee and hit the leg of the table, a frail home-made structure which lurched violently to one side and sent the lamp crashing to the floor.

Oil flew in all directions, setting fire to the sheepskin rug. In a moment everyone was so busy extinguishing the flames that prayers were forgotten.

When the confusion quieted down, Mrs. Gibson said to her husband, "Thar, Pa, see what you done! I'm alwa's a tellin' you to pull off them thar big boots o' you'rn when you come into the house."

"Why, Melvinie, did I do that? I don't see how I could when I was clean t'other side o' the fireplace, and I don't recollect a hittin' nothin'.'"

"Well, Tom, of course you hit it. You don't reckon the lamp up and jumped off the table an' nobody tetchin' it, do you? Mary, you'll have to light the lantern for the preachers to go to bed by. Thar, Pa, don't look so worried. We'll borrow another lamp to-morrow from ol' Miss Watson. She's got two. Good night, young men. Thar's extra kiver on the trunk."

Alone in their room with the door closed, Jim turned savagely upon Sam.

"What the devil ails you? I didn't know you could be such a blamed idiot. A nice preacher's son, you! Don't even know the difference between the Lord's Prayer and the Twenty-third Psalm!"

"Blame it all, Jim, if you're so set on someone preaching, why don't you do it yourself? If we were to start a revival, about the time we got the blamed thing going, the real Ashton'ud turn up."

"Don't worry about him. His horse probably stumbled and threw him over a cliff on his way to the station. If so, he'll never be heard of any more. As for my preaching, who'd sing? You can't carry a tune—"

"Jim, this thing is absurd. I don't even know to what church I belong, or whether I believe in sprinkling or deep water."

"That's easy. Keep clear of doctrines. Preach common sense. You always could put across anything you ever tried in the way of a speech, and you'd make a cracking good preacher."

"They say there's no use resisting a call to the ministry. So here goes, his Satanic Majesty might just as well bid adieu to the Dark Ridge school district. This country has never seen such a preacher as the Reverend Ashton will be."

"Bully for you! I knew you'd get your heart right, and now, Kate's for the songs! Hurrah, for the Ashton-Kates revival!"

Thus opened the "big meetin'" in the Dark Ridge school house, an unpainted one-roomed building furnished with home-made benches. Sam made up in enthusiasm and originality what he lacked in knowledge of the Scriptures. The young people crowded into the choir. Jim, who always stood near the organist to find the place for her, put into the singing of the hymns all the pep which he was accustomed to use when leading the college yells. Old Sister Raby said that she never had heard "no sich" singing, and it didn't sound quite like church music, but she supposed it was a new style and all right. Anyway, this was the first time she'd ever been able to get her son Emanuel to church without using force. Now he was always the first one ready.

So all went well until one afternoon Sam chose for his text, "Wine is a mocker, strong drink is raging; and whosoever is deceived thereby is not wise." On the way home Jim remarked, "Something was wrong with the brethren. Nobody shouted, not even Sister Raby. Maybe you better try a different theme to-morrow."

"Tomorrow I'll preach on Heaven," replied Sam.

That night after services, a stranger approached and said that he wanted to talk with the preacher. Since his new friend carried a lantern, Sam allowed the others to go ahead.

This pleased Jim as it gave him an opportunity to talk with Mary. But to-night she was not herself.

"Jim," she said, "do hurry. It's going to rain. Don't you see that dark thunder cloud in the west?"

"Why, Mary, that storm is at least an hour away. Why think of storms? With you—

> Beside me singing in the wilderness—
> Oh, Wilderness were Paradise enow!"

"Jim," said Mary impatiently, "your talk is well enough when all is right. But I tell you there's more than a thunder storm brewing to-night."

"Why, Mary, what's wrong? Don't you know that no harm can touch you when I am here?"

"Oh, it isn't myself. Listen, Jim, do you know who the man is that stopped Mr. Ashton?"

"I believe he said his name was Reece."

"Yes, he is Bill Reece, a moonshiner. Just before supper I was in the upper pasture, looking after the young lambs. I grew tired and sat down on a boulder to rest. Directly I heard voices back of the cliff and I listened. It was Bill and two other men, and they were angry about the sermon Mr. Ashton preached. I couldn't hear all they said, but I got the word 'Flat Rock,' and guessed the rest."

"Mary, why did you not tell me sooner?"

"You had all left for church when I reached home; but I did bring these," and throwing back her wrap she disclosed two revolvers. Handing one to Jim she said, "Here take this, and follow me."

For some moments after the others left them, neither Sam nor Mr. Reece said much. Sam believed that his friend wanted spiritual advice, so waited for him to state his case. At length, when they were far behind the crowd, Mr. Reece said, "I jist wanted to talk with you about that sermon you preached this afternoon."

"Were you there?" asked Sam. "I don't remember seeing you."

"No, I warn't exactly thar, not in person. I war thar by proxy, and I want to say that so long as you preached about lovin' yer neighbors, and a turnin' the other cheek, and the woman what turned to salt, no harm ain't did. But when you gits a talkin' like ye done this afternoon someone mought take hit serious, and Old Bill ain't a goin' to stand for no sich doctrin' gettin' scattered about Dark Ridge."

Sam looked down the long trail which led towards Mr. Gibson's house. Not a single lantern shone in any direction.

"Now you needn't bother to call fer help," said Bill, and he placed his hand on his hip pocket. At the same time two men stepped out of the thicket at the edge of the trail.

"Jist you come along of us an' the quieter you keep, the healthier it'll be fer ye."

Seeing no possible escape, Sam obeyed; and for almost an hour they followed a rough mountain path over boulders and through dense thickets. Then at last they came out upon a large flat rock covered with a carpet of soft gray moss and extending over about an acre of ground. At the further edge of the rock was an enormous oak tree and a few yards from it a tall, straight sapling. These two trees were the only break in the tangled growth of underbrush.

Bill brought his captive to the center of the opening. He then hung the lantern on a limb, and taking from his pocket a stout cord he bound Sam hand and foot. One of the other men fixed a slip-noose in the end of a clothes line he had been carrying, and put the loop around Sam's neck. In the meantime, the third man had climbed the sapling and was bending it downward towards the rock where the company stood.

Now for the first time Sam spoke.

"What are you going to do with me?" he asked.

"Wal, young man," replied Bill, "I reckon we're goin' to give you a free pass to that country ye preach about 'where saints immortal dwell'."

"But, don't you know that the courts will handle you for this?"

A harsh laugh came from the lips of the mountaineer.

"Wal, now, young man, that sure is a good'un. For thirty-five year, the courts hain't been able to locate

[251]

Ol' Bill. Two or three times they thought they'd got their hand on him, but alwa's he weren't thar."

"But, Bill," said Sam, playing for time, and remembering his rôle as preacher. "Even if you are unpunished here, there is a judgment which none can escape."

"That," said Bill, "is fer you to be thinkin' about, not me."

"But surely you will give me time to say a prayer," said Sam.

"Young man, ain't ye a preacher? A preacher's supposed to be ready to fly to heaven without waitin' to pray."

"Well, Bill, if I must hang I must. But just let me say a little prayer for you before I go."

"Wal, now, I'll be gol-darned, you *are* a good'un. I'd be real glad to grant your dyin' request, but we've got to hurry for the storm is about here, and it's a goin' to be a rip-starver. So you'll have to pray as you go up."

Hereupon, he threw the end of the rope to the man in the tree.

The lantern gave a feeble glow by which one could little more than distinguish the forms of the four men. Outside the narrow radius of the lantern's rays all was inky blackness, save when a sudden flash lit up the heavens and threw a vivid light upon the scene.

The rope was passed around the limb. Bill and his companion had stepped back a few steps from Sam, who faced his fate with much the same resignation he had shown when he entered the ministry. But suddenly a voice sounded on the night air. It was the voice of a woman.

"Stop! The first one who moves is a dead man."

All eyes turned in the direction from which the voice came, and in the dim light of the lantern distinguished the form of a man and a woman, each armed with a pistol.

The man in the tree almost lost his balance. Bill and his companion on the ground fell back a few steps nearer the great oak. At that moment a ball of fire seemed to fall in their midst. The earth trembled. The pistol fell from Mary's powerless hand. For a moment there was the brightness of day, then a crash of falling timbers, a deluge of rain, and darkness broken only by the feeble light from the two lanterns.

No one realized what had happened. All were shocked and unable to move. Then another flash of lightning disclosed the oak tree lying prostrate, its mighty trunk split into pieces, and near its fallen body groveled Bill and his companion.

Mary was the first to recover her composure, and rushing forward, she placed her lantern on the ground and knelt beside the prostrate moonshiner, while the torrents still descended.

"Bill," she cried, "Bill, be ye hurt?"

In her excitement she lapsed into the vernacular of her childhood.

"Wal, I reckon I'm done fer, Mary. I wouldn't a thought you'd a did it." And Bill gave a groan as he half lifted himself on his elbow and dragged his helpless limbs a few feet in a fruitless effort to stand.

"Bill," said Mary, "Bill, I ain't never did it. I didn't shoot. Something wrenched the pistol from my hand. It's the Lord what done this. Look, He's struck the oak tree with lightning. Oh, Bill, ef ye be dyin', can't you repent?"

"No, Mary, hit's too late now. Even ef the Lord'ud have me, which 'tain't likely He'd do, they'd all soon find out up thar that a mistake had been made. It wouldn't be fair nohow. I'd better jist go on whar I've started. It will probably suit me better. But, Mary, I never aimed to really kill the preacher. I was jist a fixin' to scare him away. I ain't never felt so queer. I must be a dyin'," and Bill fell back upon the ground.

Then silence followed—at last Bill spoke again.

"Mary," he said to the girl who still knelt by his side in the pouring rain, "why don't I die? It 'pears like I feel better. Holp me up. I believe I can stand."

Slowly and painfully with Mary's help, Bill got to his feet.

As soon as Jim realized what had happened, he quickly cut the cords which bound Sam's wrists and ankles and together they went to help the other man, who also was only shocked.

For a moment Bill looked around, dazed. Then he spied the man sitting in the top of the sapling, too much overcome by fear and superstition to move.

"You blamed idiot," said Bill, "what are you a settin' up thar fer? Ain't ye got no sense or is ye done growed to the limb?" Then addressing the others he said:

"It looks like you'd all be gittin' in out o' the rain. Mary, take your lantern and show these young fellers the way home. We'll come as soon as we can get that confounded idiot down."

On the following day, Sam planned to preach his sermon about Heaven, but while the choir was singing the last verse of "Beulah Land," Bill and his gang entered the house and took seats in the rear. Immediately all thoughts of heaven fled from Sam's mind, and he changed his subject to "Hell." He drew a picture of the Infernal regions which would have done credit even to Dante. Sam was naturally gifted in speech, and as he warmed up to his subject he played mightily upon the emotions of his congregation. They sat with wide eyes and half-open mouths. Occasionally a woman covered her face with her hands and sobbed. Sam kept his eyes fastened upon Bill as he gave the invitation for those to come forward who would escape the wrath to come.

Then the choir began singing,

"Oh, you must be a lover of the Lord or you can't go to
    Heaven when you die,"

and old Bill, coming down the aisle, flung himself on his knees at the mourners bench. Sister Raby began to shout, "Amen! The Lord have mercy!" and Sam said, "Let us pray."

When the prayer ended, Bill, coming up with a shout, leaped upon the mourners' bench, and waving his arms wildly in the air, called back to his gang:

"I've got hit fellers, I've got hit. What you a hangin'
around back thar fer, jist like ye don't need no religion?
A pretty lot you are! Ye ain't foolin' nobody. The
Lord, He knows you fer a low-lived bunch just the
same as I do, and the next time he strikes ye with
lightning, you'll be dead fer sure. Then whar'll ye
be? Ye'll be a wishin' that ye'd a give the devil the
slip while ye had a chance, fer when ye once gits into
Hell the Lord Hisself can't fish ye out."

From that day forth there was no question of the
success of the meeting. People came from far and
near to hear the young preacher who had converted
Bill and his gang. They came on horseback and in ox-
carts, and one man and his wife walked eight miles,
carrying their six-weeks-old twins in their arms and
driving the milk cow. They put up in the community
until the meeting closed.

It was the day following the conversion of Bill, that
Mary and Jim returning from the post office brought
a letter for Mr. Gibson. The arrival of a letter was
quite an event and would have created some comment,
but on this particular afternoon it had taken some two
hours longer than usual to walk the half mile to the
post office and back. Thus it was milking time when
they arrived and Mary, handing the letter to her
father, hastened to the pasture. Jim went with her.
Sam, who was on the porch preparing his evening sermon, suddenly looked up to find Mr. Gibson gazing
at him with a troubled expression, while in his hand
was the opened letter. It was so evident that the letter
brought some disturbing message that Sam ventured
to say:

"I hope you have not received bad news."

"Wal, no," said Mr. Gibson, "not exactly bad news, jist somethin' I can't quite understand."

"Could I help you?"

"Wal, I calculate maybe you mought, Mr. Ashton, but I won't pester ye about hit jist now," and folding the letter, he put it into the inside breast pocket of his coat. In the days that followed the old man often looked at Sam with the same puzzled expression. Once coming up unexpectedly, Sam found Mr. Gibson re-reading the letter, which he immediately folded and replaced in his inside pocket.

Two weeks passed and it was the closing day of the revival. The school house was packed. The services had begun when a stranger entered the door and, as there were no seats vacant, stood just inside.

He was a tall, thin man with shaggy eyebrows which overshadowed keen, deep-set, gray eyes. Beneath the high cheek bones, the cheeks were sunken and his complexion was bronzed by exposure to the sun. His mustache was long and pointed. His suit, which was cut in ministerial style, was shiny from long use and the trousers bagged at the knees. He wore a cellu-loid collar without a tie, and in his hand he carried a much battered, brown pasteboard satchel.

Sam had decided to make this final service an experi-ence meeting. Many of the congregation told how they had been blessed. Bill re-told the story of the thunder storm. Sister Raby both wept and shouted as she praised the Lord. When there was a pause in the testimonies, the choir filled in with a verse from "Father's gone to Glory." At last, it seemed that all were through. When the choir stopped singing no one rose to speak.

"Does any one else have a word for us?" asked Sam, from his seat back of the teacher's desk.

Then the stranger, stationed near the door, spoke. Instantly all eyes were fixed upon him.

"Is this the Dark Ridge schoolhouse?"

"It is, sir."

Thereupon he walked down the aisle to the stage, his shoes pounding and squeaking at every step. He deposited the pasteboard satchel on the stage near the desk; and, turning, faced the congregation. His voice shook with emotion.

"Brethren," he said, "I am Ashton, Stanley Ashton, preacher of the Hamburg circuit. I was sent here by Elder Norton to hold a revival at this place. What do I find? A deceiver, a viper, a wolf in sheep's clothing. Beware of false prophets!" He pointed a long, bony, accusing finger at Sam, "It were better for you that a millstone were hanged about your neck and that you were drowned in the depths of the sea. Is Brother Gibson here?"

All eyes turned to the corner where Mr. Gibson seemed to be trying to hide behind Brother Jones, but no one moved.

"If Brother Gibson is here, will he stand?"

Slowly Mr. Gibson got to his feet, guilt written on every feature. "Brother Gibson, did you not receive a letter two weeks ago, stating that I had been delayed and could not arrive for several weeks?"

Mr. Gibson shifted uneasily from one foot to the other. He fixed his gaze on a crack in the floor. His right hand unconsciously sought the inside pocket of his coat. At last he cleared his throat and said:

"You ask did I receive a letter from Brother Norton two weeks ago. Wal, no, I never. A little *more'n* two weeks ago I got a letter what said to meet Preacher Ashton and his song leader at Blue Crest of a Wednesday followin'; I done this, and found these here two young fellers a waitin' fer me. And ef you be Ashton as ye claim, then I'd like fer the young preacher to tell us who he mought be."

The crowd shifted its gaze to Sam, who slowly rose and wearing the expression of a martyr came forward. He stood a moment as though reluctant to speak.

Sister Raby leaned over and whispered to Mrs. Bumgarner, "I alwa's knowed he didn't look like no preacher I ever seen before. I jist felt from the first that somethin' was wrong. This new feller's a heap more like the preachers we alwa's had, and he's quoted more Scripture in the last ten minutes than the young man has all the two weeks he's been a preachin'. I've felt this a comin' all the time."

"Why, Sister Raby, and you've shouted more'n anybody."

But now Sam began to speak. He was perfectly calm, but his voice and manner betrayed injured pride and deep sorrow.

"Brethren and sisters of the Dark Ridge church, for two weeks I have gone in and out among you. I have eaten at your tables, and talked with you at your firesides. I have prayed and labored in your behalf. I have learned to know and love you. You have seen my work and heard my message. Now, I leave my case in your hands. If you decree that I shall go out at the bidding of a stranger whom you know not, I submit to your will, but never will I raise my voice in self-defense. If the life which I have lived among you, and the work which I have done, and the love which you bear me, do not plead my cause let me go away forever. But I wish to ask that sometimes in the quiet hours of twilight you will think of one who has loved you and who will still love you even though rejected."

Overcome by his emotions, Sam drew his handkerchief from his pocket and wiped his eyes. Then after several ineffective efforts to speak, he stretched out his hands to the audience, and said, "I await your verdict, but never shall I weaken my cause by so much as a word of explanation."

The silence which followed was broken by subdued sobs from various parts of the house. Even the stranger did not speak at once. But he was first to recover from the spell.

"Deceiver, dost thou persist in thy headlong course to destruction? Thou shalt not live out half thy days."

Sam folded his arms and stood with closely compressed lips before his accuser. But now, Bill Reece was upon his feet.

"Did you say Elder Norton sent you here to hold a revival?" he asked.

"He did," was the reply.

"Then suppose you go back and tell Brother Norton that we're much obleged, but that the Lord done got clean ahead of him, and sent a man what got on the job two weeks afore you did, an' run the devil clean out of Dark Ridge. And tell him that the Lord Hisself has split us the timbers for a church house an' in it we're a goin' to put one o' them thar painted winders to the memory of this here young man. And we ain't particular what his name is, nor who his folks is, fer we don't set much by fam'ly connections in this country. You see, we do know where he gits his orders. An' lookie here," the mighty fist of Bill was now in the face of the new preacher, "maybe you'd better start with that thar message right away, fer these here high tops ain't healthy fer some folks after the sun goes down."

As Bill talked he kept advancing towards the bewildered Ashton who retreated before him towards the door. Once only he spoke, "The Lord will avenge his servant."

"Oh, don't worry about that. We'll fix hit up with the Lord. You just *git*." And Aston and his satchel disappeared through the door.

As Bill returned down the aisle, the choir started singing, "'Tis the Old Time Religion," and Sister Raby shouted, "Bless the young preacher, I alwa's says he's jist like the Lord Jesus." A dozen voices joined hers in the Hallelulah which followed.

The collection amounted to sixty-four dollars and eighty-five cents, an unheard of sum for Dark Ridge. Bill, himself, so they said, put in twenty-five dollars.

The last good-byes had been said and only Bill lingered for a final word with Sam.

"Preacher," he said, "I know they mought be a heap o' reasons why a young feller moughtn't want folks a knowin' his name and jest who he is an' all his business; and I don't know you'rn, but I do know this, that the spirit o' the Almighty's upon ye, and I want to shake hands with the finest Christian gentlemen we've ever had in these here parts."

For once Sam's eyes failed to meet those of the mountaineer.

"Bill," he said, "I'm a long way from being what you believe me. But, old fellow, when you hear from me next, I hope to be a piece up the road."

"Wal, then," said Bill, "I reckon we've hit the same trail, only your way is blazed out ahead o' you, while Ol' Bill can't quite see through the underbrush to whar his'n's goin' to be. And he'll alwa's have to travel hit with a haltin' step 'case he ain't got no larnin'. But ef ye're ever needin' help, jist call on Bill."

Early next morning the boys started for the station. Mr. Gibson took them to the town of Walkalamoore, where they would take the train.

When Mary went to straighten up their room, she found a note addressed to herself. As she read it the color deepened in her cheeks. She pressed it to her lips. Then thinking she heard a step outside, she quickly thrust it into the front of her shirtwaist. The Bible was lying open on the table. She stopped to close it. As she did so, she found under the lid a small parcel, with an attached note which read, "Use this to help in building the new church." The package contained sixty-four dollars and eighty-five cents.

When Mr. Gibson returned from town and heard how the young men had left the entire collection, he sat for a long time looking into the fire. Then he said, "Them young men must a give away all they had fer they sold their watches at Walkalamoore. Them is the most spiritual-minded preachers we ever had." And while Mary and her mother washed the supper dishes, the old man, sitting along by the fire, drew a letter from his inside coat pocket and dropped it into the flames.

THE MARCH WIND

BY

EDNA BAKER SCRIMGER

Entered in the 1923 Contest

THE MARCH WIND

The March Wind is a wild wind
Cleaner than sky or sea;
The March Wind is a wild wind
Who frolics with boisterous glee!—
He rushes boldly upon me
And tosses my tousled hair,
His rough caresses rouge my cheeks
As we dance to his whistled air.

The March Wind is a mad wind—
Mad with the rapture of life;
He thrills my heart with his madcap joy
And the lilt of his Aeolian fife;
Utterly glad with my hand in his
Blithely we whirl away—
Out to the very edge of things,
To the birth of a fadeless day!

The March Wind is a brave wind,
Brave as the olden knights;
He carries me off in his swaying arms
Through valleys and over heights;
Out to the clear, clean places,
Out where my soul is free!
To the open, sea-swept spaces
The March Wind carries me!

ALTERNATIVE

BY

JOY KIME BENTON

——

Entered in the 1923 Contest

ALTERNATIVE

I no more wish to bind your love
Than I would wish to gyve the sea,
Or seal the perfume in the rose,
Or fetter anything that's free.

For Duty is the crooked claw
A live thing fastens on a dead—
And looking into other eyes
My heart grows strangely comforted.

CYNTHIA'S VOYAGE

BY

MRS. RICHARD B. WILLIS

———

Entered in the 1923 Contest

CYNTHIA'S VOYAGE

PHILIP, HERE'S a letter which quite takes my breath away! Mrs. Galbraith has asked us to take Cynthia Cosgrove to Europe with us. Some way had to be found to get her to her mother, I suppose, and we seem to be the way."

"Well, we can take care of her, can't we?"

"Why Phil, how can we be sure of her being suitably provided for? I admit that I am so torn up over your being ordered to the front that I don't feel very eager to be responsible for her. Mrs. Gailbraith says that Cynthia is a dear, sweet girl but rather scatter-brained. I can imagine easier tasks than taking charge of a scatter-brained girl!"

"She won't annoy you, Louise. There will be very little social life on the steamer and you and she can sit together and knit. Or we may find one other to make up a table of bridge. Her mother is perhaps lonely in London with her only son at the front; try to remember that."

It was in the early fall of 1914 when England, the great mother, was summoning her sons from all quarters of the globe. Thousands had already sailed from Canadian ports and now Colonel Kirkland, of the Field Artillery, had been called.

Three days before the sailing of the *Queen Anne* from Montreal, while Mrs. Kirkland was in the midst of her preparations to leave, she was informed that Miss Cosgrove and her maid were below. With a slight pucker in her brows and some dawning criticism in her heart, Mrs. Kirkland entered her reception room to find herself seized in the embrace of a white-robed girl and squeezed until her ribs ached.

"You dear, lovely lady to be willing to take me to mamma! It's an out-and-out act of Christian charity. I was just getting desperate! Let me look at you! You do look so sweet and motherly and satisfying. I just adore you!" Here followed a second tempestuous embrace.

Mrs. Kirkland was fairly swept off her feet. It was impossible to resist the girl gazing at her with violet eyes from beneath a white hat and filmy veil. The chaperone surrendered promptly.

"We are delighted to have you with us, dear child. I am sure we shall have good times together. However, Colonel Kirkland had some trouble in getting accommodations for you. He simply could not get a state-room for you by yourself."

"How exciting! Who am I going to draw? Is it to be an old maid or a winsome widow?"

"You could never guess, Cynthia. It is not exactly an old maid or a widow. There *is* an old-maid, Miss Cazort, but she positively refuses to have a room-mate. The only alternative is Sister Candida, a sister-of-charity on her way to the front to nurse the wounded. Can you stand that, do you think?"

"Oh, gorgeously! for I know the old maid would have given me the daily jim-jams."

When Cynthia was told that she must leave her maid behind, she bore it "equanimously" to use her own expression. It would take more than losing maids to dim the glow of her optimism.

The nun proved to be a rather colorless personality, kindly and quiet. Cynthia's steamer trunk was finally ensconced in the stateroom and her dainty little belongings placed in what she considered her moiety of space. Worn out by the excitement of the day, Cynthia retired early, safe in the efficacy of Sister Candida's prayers.

At breakfast the next morning, Miss Cazort, the solitary old maid, developed an unexpected amount of congeniality. She laughed and chatted with the little group and finished by proposing a daily game of bridge. Thereafter a part of each evening was spent in battle royal between Colonel Kirkland and Cynthia on the one hand, and Mrs. Kirkland and Miss Cazort on the other. Cynthia's lusty crow of triumph could be frequently heard, and Sister Candida, gliding about the great salon would smile leniently at the spirits of the girl.

On the third morning, Cynthia was found on deck unusually early, her chestnut curls tucked away under a blue velvet cap and her slender figure almost lost in her long, loose coat. The cabin was stuffy, she said, and she had come out for fresh air.

During the hours of that day she and Miss Cazort evinced a noticeable enjoyment of each other's society, which culminated before the day was over in a request for Mrs. Kirkland's permission to transfer Cynthia's belongings to the stateroom of Miss Cazort.

Her Holiness, Sister Candida, had been most kind and considerate, Cynthia averred, but there *were* more enlivening experiences than that of hobnobbing with a lady wrapped in mystic trances and addicted to long periods of silence. Even the sister herself could not blame her for exchanging the sanctity of a cloister for the geniality and the bridge-playing qualities of Miss Cazort. Furthermore, Cynthia intended to continue pleasant relations with Sister Candida, who must not be allowed to feel herself deserted.

Pursuant to her purpose of friendliness, Cynthia often sought the companionship of the lonely nun "in order to keep her from having a nervous collapse over her vow-brooding." Together they might sometimes be seen watching the sunset glow on the waves or pacing the moonlit deck in the evening.

"Mamma Kirkland," cried Cynthia one day, "her Holiness is strictly cultured and clever. It's like pulling the jaw-teeth of a whale to get her to talk, but her tongue surely wags and wiggles when she does begin. She has told me more about fairies and nixes and water-sprites on the Rhine and demons on the Brocken than my weak noddle can hold. I have actually gazed on Undine weeping in the coral caves of the Elbe for that scamp, Hildebrand. Oh, and alas, why do women love men better than men love women?"

"Perhaps her Holiness herself has been disappointed in love. That may account for her vocation."

"Perhaps so. I never thought of that," said Cynthia, thoughtfully.

Nothing of note transpired during the rather monotonous voyage. Once the captain thought he had sighted a submarine, and for a few hours excitement reigned on the *Queen Anne*. During the moments of suspense Cynthia stood between Mrs. Kirkland and Sister Candida. If she had to be blown into eternity, she remarked, she wished to be in company with her devout Holiness before being reduced to molecules. On this occasion Sister Candida herself showed more tendency to the excitement of ordinary mortals than at any previous time. She looked fixedly through her field-glasses, then lifted her hands again and again in a fashion doubtless peculiar to her order, seeming to implore the protection of Heaven in this critical moment. The mysterious looking object soon disappeared and the daily routine of life re-asserted itself.

At Liverpool the breaking up of the party who had sailed together was more or less solemn, for it was unlikely that the chances of war would ever re-unite them. Mrs. Kirkland embraced Cynthia tenderly, telling her mother that she had been the sunshine of the voyage. Colonel Kirkland patted her on the shoulder, emphasizing his fatherly touch with the remark that he wished she were his daughter. Miss Cazort told Cynthia that she had changed what might have been a stiff, ceremonious acquaintanceship into a merry house-party. Even the spiritual depths of Sister Candida's soul seemed stirred beyond their wont. She

said simply, but not without emotion, "Good-bye, dear
child. May God bless you and give you your heart's
desire!" She then kissed the girl's snowy brow and
turning away, was soon lost in the throng.

Mrs. Cosgrove's maternal pride was naturally pleased
with these expressions of love and admiration. After
cordial thanks to Colonel and Mrs. Kirkland and to
Miss Cazort, she accompanied Cynthia to their car and
they too were soon an atom in a great crowd. In the
subsequent ride, Cynthia was bubbling over with tears
of joy and of farewell. She learned that her brother
Edward, now in the trenches, was in good health and
spirits though fully aware that he stood in the shadow
of death. Youth is optimistic, even in the face of
danger.

* * * *

A year had passed. Countless souls had been swept
into eternity, countless prayers had ascended to God.
Edward Cosgrove had been wounded and was too ill
to be moved from the hospital at the front. Immediately on learning of this, Mrs. Cosgrove and Cynthia
had gone to attend him. In their daily care of the
wounded boy, many another lonely soldier felt the
cheer of their presence and the healing of their wom-
anly sympathy. Cynthia's face had lost much of its
gaiety but none of its beauty. Her cheeks were now
more suggestive of the lily than of the rose, and her
great violet eyes seemed to look into the unknown
future with a despairing questioning of fate. She
manifested no elation at the victories of the Allies, only

a yearning pity for the dying and wounded on both sides. When she went out for her daily exercise, she often visited the camps of the prisoners; no line of race or caste seemed to present a barrier to the flood-tide of her vast compassion.

The truth was that the iron hand of war was falling with terrific weight upon the heart of the girl. Her mother watched her with alarm and, seeing her form growing more slender daily, suggested sending her back to their friends in London. But a startlingly positive refusal put an end to all such discussion. Once when reading of a desperate charge in which a certain German regiment had been cut to pieces, she fainted. Soon rallying, she insisted that she was as well as ever and against her mother's protest resumed her daily visits to hospital and camp.

Her brother being now on the road to recovery, Cynthia was often accompanied by her mother on her errands of mercy. Mrs. Cosgrove now felt more alarm for the fragile girl than for the plucky young soldier. One day after the British troops had made a very successful charge the two were passing through the wards of a hospital for German prisoners. Moans of the sufferers filled the air, and as Mrs. Cosgrove caught a glimpse of Cynthia's tense expression, she exclaimed:

"Come, let us go. This is a long drawn-out agony for you. You simply can't stand it."

The girl did not even hear her mother. Her wide eyes were fixed upon a young German officer who had just been brought in on a stretcher. As they laid him on a cot, his face was turned towards her. With a timid step she moved nearer. The officer opened his eyes and groaned in terrible suffering. With a cry that might have come from the heart of Iphegenia as she lay on the altar and looked on her father's face, Cynthia staggered forward and fell senseless to the floor. When she revived, she found herself upon a rude bench, her head in her mother's lap. She lifted her eyes with a gaze of such imploring pathos that Mrs. Cosgrove was startled. "Oh, mother, mother!" were her only words.

"What is it, Cynthia darling? Tell mother!"

"Mother, I think it is Max!" Again she almost relapsed into unconsciousness.

Finally Cynthia rose and walked to the cot on which lay the wounded soldier. His eyes were closed.

"Max!" she called. Her voice, strained in her effort at self-control, grew more piercing in its intensity. "Max, speak to me!"

The young Saxon opened a pair of deep blue eyes and looked around him. When his glance met Cynthia's, a glow of indescribable joy came over his face.

"Cynthia, is it you, at last?" His hand stirred feebly. The girl dropped on her knees and with the tender note of a dove to her young, murmured his name with terms of endearment almost inaudible. When their eyes met in full recognition, the intensity of his gaze made her for the moment oblivious of surroundings. His countenance also plainly indicated the rapture he was too weak to express. With an air of awed solemnity, Cynthia leaned forward and pressed her lips to his. There was a strange look upon both faces, a look of joy in a sacramental reunion after deep waters of separation. Time was forgotten.

"Cynthia, who is this man?" asked Mrs. Cosgrove, indignation speaking in tone and gesture.

"Oh mamma, this is Max, I mean Captain Max Munsterberg, the man I love. . . Oh, wait, mamma, and let me explain! Do you remember my telling you about Sister Candida on board the *Queen Anne?*"

"Sister Candida!" murmured the amazed lady.

"Yes, mamma, this is her, I mean she. No, this is *him!*" With a suggestion of girlish giggling, Cynthia forced her mother into a chair. "Don't say a word until I tell you every thing!" she commanded. "You remember I wrote you that I was to be put into a state-room with an Ursuline nun. At first I was scared to think how devout she would be and how naughty poor little Cynthia was. The first two nights I went to sleep while she was counting her beads. The next night I went to sleep promptly but woke up later with the feeling that some one else in the room was awake too. I lay still and listened. I could see a light shining inside the curtains of Sister Candida's berth. My umbrella was standing near the head of my berth. I lifted it noiselessly and raised just a tiny edge of one of the curtains. What *do* you suppose she was doing?"

"Go on," her mother ordered, sternly ignoring Cynthia's bubbling giggles.

"Sister Candida, the holy nun, was *shaving*! Her arms were strong, her muscles looked like ropes and her beard was thick and stubby! Evidently Sister Candida was a *man*!"

"Cynthia Cosgrove, you don't mean to tell me that you staid—"

"Wait a minute, mamma, can't you? I kept as still as a mouse the rest of the night but not a wink of sleep did I get. I got up very early and went on deck. The next day I was standing alone hesitating about how to tell Mrs. Kirkland; Sister Candida came swishing along with her veils and draperies and a most peculiar expression on her face. She didn't know that I had found out any thing but her conscience was evidently getting the best of her. With a word of apology she began:

" 'Miss Cosgrove, I cannot deceive you during the remainder of this voyage. I am a German soldier on my way home to fight for the fatherland. I disguised myself in order to obtain passage on the ship of an enemy. If you betray me, I shall probably be killed as a spy. Can you and will you be silent?' "

"Notwithstanding the fact that the soldier was an enemy of my country I could and did. I went to Mrs. Kirkland with some sort of song and dance about Sister Candida's dullness. Then I wheedled Miss Cazort into inviting me to stay with her. In the evening I promenaded the deck with Sister Candida 'to keep her from feeling lonely and deserted.' Oh, mamma, I was so happy. I never knew the glory of life before; I

never felt the beauty of nature as I felt it when gazing upon sea and cloud with Max. He taught me so
many things about duty and sacrifice that he opened
up an undreamed of world to me. He comes of fine
people and, oh, mother, I love him so much."

"But Cynthia, how can you love the enemy of your
country? Think of what the German army did in
Belgium and Northern France. They were unspeakable
brutes."

"They were, and Max knows it and is desperately
ashamed of them. Mamma, you must remember that
he is not a Prussian; he is a *Saxon*! If he ever gets a
chance, I don't doubt that he'll punch old Hindenberg's
red nose for him. And I hope and pray that he'll soon
get the chance."

"Cynthia, this very man may have wounded
Edward."

"Yes, and Edward may have wounded and nearly
killed this very man! But they are both going to get
well. The point is Max and I love each other. 'What
God has joined together let no man put asunder.' No
woman would wish to, I know, 'specially my sweet,
tender-hearted mother!'"

A sob came into the tender, child-like voice. Mrs.
Cosgrove sat silent and perplexed, gazing thoughtfully
at the form, all too slender, and the young face, all
too pale. This then was what had been the matter
with her little daughter. What *ought* she to do? She
laid her hand on the soft curls of Cynthia, the silence
broken only by the moan of some suffering soldier or
by the gentle step of a nurse.

Suddenly Mrs. Cosgrove rose and took Cynthia by the hand. With a look of unspeakable yearning, of deep maternal love, she walked to the cot, took the hand of the young Saxon and placed it in that of her daughter.

SALLIE AND HER BONNET

BY

MRS. C. A. JORDAN

———

Entered in the 1923 Contest

SALLIE AND HER BONNET

When Sallie goes a walking
  Down the village street,
Her bonnet's tied beneath her chin
  In a bow so prim and neat.
It shades the glad light in her eyes,
  Her smile so sweet and bright;
The little dimples in her cheek
  Are hidden out of sight.
All this and more it hides from view,
  I glower down upon it,
And curse my tantalizing fate,
  When Sallie wears her bonnet.

But when we reach the shady lanes
  Filled with sun-flecked shadows,
And listen to the wooing winds,
  The song birds from the meadows,
Off comes this shield of straw and lace,
  I gaze my soul contented
On lively lips and snowy throat,
  And chin with dimple dented,
Her hair all gleaming molten gold,
  The sunlight full upon it.
Oh! all the world is joy and song,
  When Sallie swings her bonnet.

We wander down through shady paths,
    Across cool, rippling streams,
On through fresh and scented dells
    In a maze of golden beams.
We linger at the rustic stile,
    A thrush goes singing by;
I stoop, and try, but all in vain,—
    I seek to catch her eye;
Her hand is resting on the stile,
    I press my lips upon it,
And then—Oh! then—well, I must say,
    We both forgot the bonnet.

THE SILVER BELL

BY

MRS. AL FAIRBROTHER

———

Entered in the 1923 Contest

THE SILVER BELL

A youthful king in the olden time
Had cast a silver bell
    For the palace tower,
    Of wondrous power,
The moulders had wrought so well.
High in the arch he had it hung
Where dancing sunbeams fell,
    That whenever his joy
    Was without alloy,
The exultant note from its silver throat
Should his perfect happiness tell.

He woed a maiden pure and fair
And made her his queen—his bride;
    And he said: "Let the bell
    "My happiness tell
"That the nation may share in my pride."
But e'en as he spoke his robe was caught
By a woman who blocked his way,
    His pardon to crave
    For an abject slave.
He granted her prayer but it brought with it care
And the bell could not ring that day.

The years went by and a child was born,
In princely mould was he cast.
    Then said the king:
    "The bell shall ring
"To tell I'm happy at last."

But ere the mandate glad was given
To publish his new-found joy,
    Came news of disease
    From over the seas
Of infant biers and parents' tears,
And the father thought of his boy.

As time rolled on the victor's wreath
His honored brow oft twined,
    While in princely deeds
    A nation's needs
Were studied by sovereign kind.
But, though loved and honored and sung,
With the world and its wealth at his feet,
    There was never a time
    When the wondrous chime
Of the silver bell his people could tell
That his happiness was complete.

So every heart has a silver bell
Hung aloft in the palace of dreams,
    And the time of its ringing
    Hope ever is bringing
As bright through distance it gleams.
There through the years from childhood's hour
And its place in the noonday sun,
    It never is rung
    Till the requiem's sung—
Till it echoes the knell of the funeral bell,
Till earth is lost and heaven is won.

SILENT TREES AND SINGING MEN

BY

JOY KIME BENTON

———

Entered in the 1923 Contest

SILENT TREES AND SINGING MEN

One does not hear the exultation of the sap;
The drumming of the rising sap is never heard,
For Southern pines have stately Southern ways,
The amber in their veins is slowly stirred.

The woods hold silence, like a conch-shell, to the ear,
Small wonder that the songs the negro sings
Are fraught with undertones of wind and rain and
    sea—
Endless, minor-cadenced, unbeginning little things.

Oh, care-free people born of melody and mirth,
And cradled in the sun since time began,
One listens to your haunting ancient pipes
And looks beneath the trees for tracks of Pan.

THE MINSTREL SINGS

BY

LAURA BURTON MILLER

—

Entered in the 1923 Contest

THE MINSTREL SINGS

No gift of gold for my lady,
No jewel that restless gleams,
Only a bit of a love song,
Woven of beauty and dreams.

Poignant and simple and tender,
Blended of roses and rue,
Merry, since so you would have it,
Sad, because it is true.

You are the radiant star-shine,
I but the candle light,
Merely a wandering minstrel,
Singing into the night.

Yet—who knows, perchance, my lady
Some hour fate yet may bring,
When you will sigh remembering
This little song I sing.

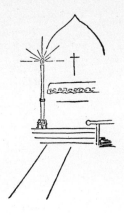

NON OMNIS MORIAR

BY

EMILY F. SHAPIRO

———

Entered in the 1923 Contest

NON OMNIS MORIAR

Eternal night; the sable mist
Of death, the chill of everlasting
Winter creeps around the heart;
No light is here, no warmth,
No laughter, nor the gladdening voice
Of friends, the sweet dear intimacy of home.

No light; no more the vivid gleams
Of the sun's warm rays bring cheer and comfort,
Pour forth the warm hot tide of life
In leaping brooks.
But slow decay, the rot and moulder,
The gnawing tooth of time, the feeding worm,
Break down the flesh that gleamed,
Once white and triumphant in its beauty.

Prepotent night,
Black, without hope, the breath of life
Gone forever.
No light.
No warmth.
But all is cold and dark,
Full of the blackness of despair
Shrouded in a mantle of oblivion.
Silent, and without life.

Save one small gleam, a candle
Burning bright, the cloth, an altar,
And that insistent voice:
"I shall arise!"

IN MEMORIAM

POEMS

by

Mrs. Charles Ives

Echoes

Limitations
(Honor poems, 1913)

Research
(First honor, 1915)

At Night
(First honor, 1916)

Small Town Memories
(Awarded the Separk Cup, 1921)

Modus Operandi
(Honorable mention, 1922)

Hannah Allen Ives (1863-1923) was born in Greensboro, but lived all her life in New Bern, her ancestral home, where her high Christian principles as well as her splendid literary and artistic ability were ever at the service of her Church and her town.

With a quiet manner she seemed always to win the deference of others. Informed, exact and thorough was her knowledge along unusual lines; for she was a voracious and constant reader, loving trees, birds and all natures, as well as art and music.

Being possessed of unusual musical ability, she was frequently called upon for the leading and training of others. A pioneer in the Woman's Club work of New Bern, her literary taste set always a high standard.

She bore with fortitude and without complaint her years of ill health; and even in her last years of real illness, her interest in human kind, keen sense of humor, and radiance of spirit drew many to her for guidance.

ECHOES

"The sound of a voice that is still."

They say that when an ancient violin—
Time-mellowed, trained by a master's hand
To thrill 'twixt measured notes in harmony,
To vibrate unto perfect utterance
Of his inspired, melodious thought—they say
That when untouched it lies, in quiet room,
E'en though unstretched the strings,
An ear laid gently o'er may hear soft tones,
Sweet murmurings, and faint vibrations, as
The voiceful instrument croons musingly
Within its heart, a melody long hushed.

*   *   *   *

My house of life has now an empty room,
And when I enter it, half listening
For songs I used to hear, so still it is!
But while I wait, there comes as in a dream
Soft murmurings, and sweet low whisperings,
And gentle promptings to my soul of better things—
A tender word, perhaps, for one who grieves,
A new compassion for the foot that strays,
Things sweet and good that rise above my mind,
Things wise and fine that soar beyond my thoughts;
And marveling, I know they're not mine own,
But that they float as breathing echoes from
The silenced earthy music of the twain
Whose Heaven-taught hearts lie now with severed
    strings
Low in the breathless mould.

LIMITATIONS

O for the mountain heights! Alas, the steeps
I cannot climb to-day! The heart which so
Reluctant throbs on level ways, would ne'er
Consent to take unto itself new toil.
Still, one fair morn I climbed, 'neath summer skies,
On, up, through bracken and through bloom of flower,
To a great rock—the crest of th' earth it seemed—
And saw (and in my heart the picture lives
Forever-more,) all things: the universe
Receding from mine eyes to bounds unknown—
Billow on billow, wave on wave—a sea
Of world, a world of sea!

I cannot music wake, such as I love!
My trembling fingers' strength doth not suffice
To downward hold the ivories that check
The organ's pulsing breath;—likewise the feet
That falter in their daily task, cannot
Release the diapason's wondrous depth.
Still, in my soul of souls live harmonies
That ever singing wind and touch and part,
Like music of the spheres, whose circling tracks
Do meet, and part to meet again, in wide
Appointed years. And these dumb concords **vainly**
Plead for utterance.

So meagre is the voice I lift in song!
Numb, helpless, almost inarticulate
I ofttimes stand, while yet the concept of
The sound I would, is round and full and strong
As Melba ever know; full-well I read
The guiding notes, as if it were a page
Of script, and warm within my own, I feel
The intent of the master-singer's mind.
If only in the column of my throat
The vaulted chambers of the voice were firm
And smooth—and only, if the bands which bind
My breath, could trained be to strength!

And yet, though small my gifts, I have not swathed
Them in the chilling folds of discontent,
But tried to work for their increase. For in
That day when our sad limitations here
Shall all be justified, if I can say
"Dear, pitying Lord, I've done my best with this
Weak frame and what Thou didst entrust unto
Its fostering care,"—knowest thou not with me,
That in the body new which meets my soul
Upon the resurrection morn, there will be
Strength for all that I have striven for here,
The substance of life's sweet, God-given hopes!
No earthly labor shall be lost,
No dream-plan unfulfilled!

RESEARCH

*"Ah, but a man's reach should exceed his grasp,
Or what's heaven for?"*

To doubt, to dream, to dare is thine,
O Mariner, whose stately ship of thought,
Equipped against the tide of many minds
Has loosed its moorings from the shores of fact,
To sail into the night of the unknown!

Be strong of heart! Fear not to fare thee forth
Upon the uncharted sea of mystery
Which darkly flows about our consciousness!
Above earth's shifting cloud of circumstance,
Truth, like a star fixed high, sheds its pure beams
On other lands than this which fades away
Behind thy helm, along the level sky.

Faint intimations of a shore unseen
Flash for a moment in its silver light,
(Like wild, shy sea-birds, nest-tired, winging white)
Quick to be lost in gloom.
To ears attuned, the vibrant ether seems
To whisper in a faltering, alien tongue
Some half-guessed secret from an outer world;
Or on its breath to bear a precious hint
Of lore transcendent and elusive as
The fragrance of rare flowers of heart's desire.

Quick, fare thee on! It may not be so far:
This hidden, shadowy, sought and un-searched land!

A bold Columbus once, finding his world too small,
Scorning men's sneers, set sail with joy
Into the golden West, and planted there
The Cross, upon his continent of dreams.
So Galileo, high on Pisa's tower,
Impatient of the blue horizon's bounds,
Dared dream of other stars below its marge,
And breasting along a bitter tide of hate,
Toiled on until his magic glass enlarged
The universe a thousand thousand fold.

Fare on! Man's deed is bounded by his dream:
Dream greater things, and then spare not the toil!

But toil as thou wilt, alone, thou dost not win.
The final triumph is to thee a gift,
A free and royal accolade.—At times,
And in the fullness of His own good time,
God singles out a man, lifting him up
Above his fellows, from the dimness of
Their search into earth's deep and secret things,
And with a revelation brighter far
Perhaps than any dream foretold,
The All-Creator places in his hand
A key to some great mystery of the universe.

Work thou, therefore,
And consecrate such toil by prayer.—Who knows:
Perchance thou art that man!

AT NIGHT

By day,
The sapphire sky, and the pale horizon's round
Close in for us a dear familiar earth—
A little well-worn world.
But when night cometh
And the day's chimera vanishes,
The curtain lifts upon reality, and puny man looks out
And up, into great gaping gulfs of gloom,
Unmeasured and unmarked save by the stars,
Whose calm infinitude of lifted light
Speaks but to urge his fear.
At night, there are no bounds!

      *   *   *   *

I cannot rest!
The silent, star-stained darkness
Steals my sleep
And lures me from my couch
Straight to the water's edge.

It is the mid-time of the night and tide;
All scant and shallow lies the little cove.
Shore-soiled, its evening wave fled to the cleansing sea,
But now, pure, undefiled,
The flood of morn sleeps on the bar,
Waiting its turn.

No sound near by
Save purling lappings on the sandy shore!
No sound afar
Save muffled thunder of the surf upon the shingle,
Miles away, across the bay!

With stark white spars and cordage dank,
The fisher fleet
Stands by like sentinels,
Rich golden serpentinings from each anchor light,
Darting through inky shallows
To my feet!

With one hot piercing eye
A flounder boat peers round the marshes' marge,
Slips stealthily into a watery lane,
Is gone!

No breezes stir!
The weary winds sleep high in Heaven's vault,
The very stars in dimness drowse,
And seem to draw away from earth
And me!

Up, up I gaze
Into the solemn silence!
On, through the deeps of darkness,
Out—far out—of earth's small time and space,
Past suns and systems old,
And off into a fearsome nothingness!
Is there no end; no resting-place for me?
No backward drawing to the solid earth once more?

Lost twixt the waters and the sky
A gull, with beating broken wing,
Shrills out his shivering fear.

So, shuddering, send I forth my soul into the night.

"O infinite, touch me I pray!
"Thou art so high:
"So low, am I!
"Thou art so great;
"So small my day!"

There are no bounds, at night!

SMALL-TOWN MEMORIES
(School Days)

I'm glad that when I was a child
I did not have to play
On pavements laid by line,
But that I grew up in a little town
Where my eager feet, running about at will,
Could feel a friendship with the good old earth,
And tread with joy the daily way to school.

Along a pathway from our mother's door
We children ran at morn;
A pathway not too straight, nor neat enough
To frighten from their footing
In the cracks between the bricks,
The wee wild things, and tiny mosses
That were looking for the light.

Then, straight along the street
Our way led on;
Where the soft and sandy sidewalks
Fell in gracious hollows here and there,
Which were sometimes sky-pied pools of April rain
Edged with the spring's rich wind-blown pollen dust;
("Mother, what is pollen?"
"Ah, children, who can say!")
Or in the days when autumn rains
Had stripped the maples of their summer dress,
Were lined and bordered round about,
With richer gold and crimson
Than my grown-up eyes have ever seen.

[319]

And further on the way we crossed
The church yard with its osage hedge,
Which hid a cat-bird's nest,
And saw, first, lovely green-blue eggs,
And later, gaping yellow mouths.
                    (O mystery!)

And then we crossed the street
And jumped a spring-fed ditch,
Where all untended on its moss-grown shaded side,
Grew, little stiff, straight ferns,
And violets white and blue:—wild blooms
Like some we children saw once
When our mother drove us
With the old black horse, three miles
Away out past the farms and cotton fields,
Into the silent woods.
(O the marvel of it!
"How did they come to our town?
Who planted them?")

And so,—with growing wonder each new day
We went to the little school house,
And to the teacher with the strong true voice,
Who woke the love of music in my soul,
And taught us girls and boys—besides our sums—
To sing "Sweet Bye and Bye,"
And "Old Black Joe"
And "Swanee River,"
In our childish alto and soprano parts.

THE OLD NORTH STATE

I'm glad that when I was a child
No towering walls obscured my sunny or my starry
    sky,
But that homely bending roofs hovered the growing
    broods,
And wide red chimneys reared themselves
Over the little town, like friendly sentinels.

Sometimes—in summer—at the amber sunset hour,
Our mother sat upon the low back steps,
While all the children—
There were six, and baby—
Played about the grassy yard
And watched the homing swallows go to bed,
Flying   in   wheeling   whorls—around—around—
    around—
Over and over, and back again;
At last to tumble down the chimney
In a great black swirling swarm.

And then we'd rush into our house, pell mell,
To stoop down by the fire-place,
And to hear way up the big dark hole
The thunder of a hundred beating wings.

I'm glad, that when I was a child,
No handiwork of man
Had covered up for me,
The finger-prints of God.

MODUS OPERANDI

"God useth us to help each other so,
Lending our minds out!"—Browning.

There flicked across the brimming goblet
Of a poet's mind one day
A slender thread of thought
Spun from another's brain.

This, floating trailed into his consciousness;
Which like a bowl of richest, rarest wine,
Mellow with memories of cloud and sun,
Fragrant with odours from the fruit and flower,
Sparkling and sharp with the tang of frosty nights,
Held, all resolved, his life, its joy and pain;
With all that he had seen and pondered o'er,
Or dreamed to do, and dared, and failed,
Or unto blood had striven for and attained.

And straightway to the living filament
There rushed and touched, and touching clung,
Something of all these deep heart-tinctured things.
And just as glittering crystals, bit by bit
Can break from fluid super-charged, to catch
Upon a floating thread—a clustering mass;—
So sprang forth from the ripe wine of his soul
Fair crystals of the poet's rich experience:
His glowing thoughts, clustered upon their borrowed
    thread,

Breaking into a page of burning words,
Fitted, perhaps, to flash life's deeper meaning
To some hungering heart,
Or holding in their lucid depths,
To shine upon the darkened ways of earth,
A gleaming ray of the deathless fire of truth,
Which floods shall never quench
Nor the tooth of time destroy.